WILL SHAKESPEARE
& the
Globe Theater

WILL SHAKESPEARE

AND THE

GLOBE THEATER

BY ANNE TERRY WHITE

Illustrated by C. WALTER HODGES

RANDOM HOUSE · NEW YORK

To Debbie and Judy

Contents

Foreword

This book does not pretend to be a biography; for the known facts of Shakespeare's life are too few to warrant such a designation. Rather is this a reconstruction based on the facts and on assumptions that can reasonably be drawn from the facts. None of the characters has been invented; all lived and must have been a part of the poet's life. We cannot, of course, be sure that the story as told in these pages is what actually happened. But it is what may very well have happened.

ANNE TERRY WHITE

1. *To the City of His Dreams*

IN THE year 1586 a young man of two-and-twenty was riding toward London on horseback. There was nothing in his appearance to distinguish this traveler from any young university man going up to London to live by his wits. His clothes were modest, his purse was lean, his horse was a hired hack. But he was no university man. What little schooling he had experienced lay very far behind him. Yet there was that in his head and heart which would cause Will Shakespeare to leave a mark in the world—a mark such as no university man ever left before or since.

Will himself had no thought of making his mark. He was scarcely conscious of the great powers astir within him. All he knew was that he loved to put words together. All he asked was to act, and write plays, and be a part of that alluring theater world which almost as far back as he could remember had beckoned to him. And now as his horse trotted briskly along the road that was barely more than a path, his heart beat with a wild excitement. His yearning and pining and fretting were at an end. His dream of the stage was about to be fulfilled.

It was hard to believe that a few brief hours ago he had breakfasted with his wife, had kissed his three-year-old Susanna farewell, had held his twin babies Hamnet and Judith for the last time. Already his family was fading from him. Already everything in the little town of Stratford-upon-Avon seemed very far away.

Was it only yesterday that his good friend Hamnet Sadler had said to him: "My Uncle John is come from London. Now there's the hired horse to take back. If ever you mean to break away, Will, here's your chance. At the price of eight-pence a day you can ride, and with any luck at all you can be in London in three days' time."

"Hamnet," he had answered straightaway, "there is a tide in the affairs of men. Mine, I feel, is at the flood. If I do not voyage now, all my life will be bound in shallows and miseries. Come what may, I will go."

And here he was on the road. The four years of his marriage and the frictions of day to day were behind him. Well that they were. It had been a mistake from the start, his marriage with Anne Hathaway—he a lad of eighteen and she a woman of six-and-twenty. Well, he would never think unkindly of her. For the sake of some happy hours and the three children she had borne him, he would ever keep a tenderness for her. His father and mother would see to it that she was never in need, and from London he would send her money when he could. When he could. The small sum in his purse would have to serve him till he got established.

If he could but keep it safe! There were footpads abroad on the London road—he had been well warned of them. "And mounted highway-men, too," John Sadler had said. "On my way down I oft heard talk of Gamaliel Ratsey. The swaggering rascal keeps in that neighborhood now. Masked he goes, mark you, and wears a great black hat, with hoops of wrought gold in his ears. You won't mistake him, Will. And woe to you if you fall in with him, for it will help no whit to cry him mercy. There's no be-guiling him, either—in the wink of an eye your purse will change hands. And I warrant you, Will, the while he takes the Queen's silver he'll preach you as good a sermon on Christian char-ity as ever you heard in Stratford church."

No fear of meeting highwaymen yet a while, though. This was still but a track joining the small towns on the way to Oxford. And those dreaded lords of the road kept to the great highroads of England where folk with heavy purses and jeweled rings and chains of gold about their necks passed up and down.

"Yet for the sake of the footpads," thought Will, " 'twould be well to have some company by the way." And he scanned the dust for fresh cart tracks that would show a carrier was not far ahead. But all the carts he came up with were slow two-wheelers heavy with firewood, calves for the butcher, or crates of fowl going to market.

Having never been robbed, Will Shakespeare was not too apprehensive, and he soon dropped all thought of being relieved of his purse. The early spring sunshine and the new sense of freedom filled him with a joy he could scarce contain. All about him the fields were gay with crocuses and daffodils. They set his tongue rhyming so that he longed for pen and ink. When at last he stopped beside a gurgling brook, let his horse drink deep, and sat down to the bread and cheese he had brought from home, the madrigal he had been composing was complete in his head.

He had made good pace in the afternoon to assure himself of shelter before night came on. And an hour after sunset he reached the little village of Chipping Norton. There was no mistaking the inn—it was the only building with a roof of tile instead of thatch. Besides, the little balcony over the doorway, the row of dormer windows, and the noisy courtyard proclaimed the hostel quite as well as the swinging sign which read: THE PEWTER POT.

Will, all too conscious that he was but two-and-twenty, put on a careless front and did his best to act the assured and seasoned traveler. So well did he succeed that the two boys who ran out to him as soon as he turned into the yard vied with each other to serve him. One helped him alight, untied his riding bag, and led him toward the taproom. The other, who had held the bridle while Will dismounted, took over the horse and began walking the animal up and down slowly to cool him.

Will cast an uneasy glance over his shoulder. For on this point, too, John Sadler had warned him. "You'll see a fine show of service," he said, "but it's a rare hostler, believe me, that doesn't hustle your beast off into the first handy stall the instant your back is turned. Once you're out of sight, like as not all your horse will get is a scant handful of oats and a slap on the rump for hospitality."

It was pleasant to come out of the evening chill into the cheery taproom where a great fire burned on the hearth. Will took in the row on row of pewter pots hung along the walls as if to verify the hostel's name. Then he followed the boy up a flight of stairs and into a chamber at its head.

"Shall I off with your boots, sir, and have supper brought up?" the boy asked.

"Nay," Will answered. "I'm not so enamored of my own company that I would keep it all day and evening too. I'll join the guests at the common table below. But what's for supper, boy?"

"Mutton done to a turn, sir, and carrots if you've a mind to 'em."

"I've a mind to anything God made to go down gullet," said Will with a laugh.

But he would not sit down to food before he had been to the stable to see how his horse was faring. It relieved him greatly to find the boy rubbing the animal down, whistling merrily while he worked with brush and towel. Will noted with satisfaction that plenty of

fodder and a thick bed of straw had been provided. His conscience easy then, he turned to
the taproom where some dozen men were already eating at a long, uncovered table.

Will sat down among them. Forthwith a dish
of savory mutton and carrots, together with a
knife and a tankard of brimming ale, was set
before him, and he plunged into the fare with
gusto. Yet, famished though he was, he let no
word of the conversation go by him. Everything was new, everything exciting. And all of
it was strangely unreal. As he listened or joined
in the talk, as he watched the faces and gestures, it seemed to him that the carters and
drovers and merchants, the bustling host and
the potboys—yes, and he himself—were all
actors wonderfully got up for some lively play.

"All the world's a stage," he thought as he
got under the blanket that night. "And the
men and women in it are merely players. If I
could but get pat the trick of each man's
speech! Ay, and learn to read the mind's con-
struction in the face!"

He lay a long time thinking of the day's impressions. He had taken in everything as a sponge sops up water. He felt heavy with it all and yet wonderfully light as if suspended in midair. He was betwixt and between. The old was behind, the new as yet untried. How would he fare in great London among the experienced players, men like Richard Burbage and Edward Alleyn, whose fame had spread even to the provinces? More important, how would he rate with the university men who wrote the plays? There must be stiff competition in theater-mad London, and poets were doubtless two a penny. He had no scholarship, alas—small Latin and less Greek.

"Ay, but the Queen's English belongs to all," he whispered to himself. And on that happy note he fell asleep.

2. *Adventures by the Way*

WILL SHAKESPEARE awoke to the clatter of hoofs over cobbles and, recalling with a tingle of joy where he was, reached for his clothes.

His chamber, like all the upstairs sleeping rooms, opened on the inn-yard. Having dressed, he stepped out onto the gallery that ran all around the rectangle of the yard and, leaning over the railing, looked below. Two of the carters with whom he had supped the night before were taking their departure. There was hustle and bustle, a running of boys to the stable and back again, cries of "Holla!" and "Stand, I say!"

"Like a play, like a play," sang again through Will's mind. And, indeed, he knew that by far the greatest number of plays were performed in just such inn-yards. He himself had witnessed only one in such a place, for the companies that came to Stratford put on their plays in the Guildhall. But the thrill of that one inn-yard performance had never left him. At one end of the yard a stage had been set up on trestles. The inn behind had provided dressing rooms, entrances and exits. The gallery above had served as balcony. The rest of the yard had on this occasion been so crowded with spectators that they had trampled one another. But Will had come hours before the play began, paid his penny, and taken up his station at the very front.

"I might have touched the players," he thought. "And to my mind 'twas better so. To view the play from the galleries like this—for all the ease of sitting down—puts too much space between." A ripple of remembrance shot through him. He saw again the flash of sword-play, the merry sport of clowns, the mincing steps of boys dressed up as women, and heard again the mouth-filling words that lifted his heart high.

With a start he brought himself back to the day. "And what a day 'tis!" he said, smiling up at the blue sky through which snatches of white cloud sailed, blown by the winds of spring.

"I'll not spend any of my little wealth on breakfast," he thought. "I'll eat my bread as I ride."

Coming down, saddlebag in hand, he called for his horse, carefully counted out his score, and having satisfied his thirst at the pump, mounted his horse. He made a grand exit toward the gate, but spoiled it by a wink at the potboy.

Will was soon on the main road to Oxford, and here the carriers' carts were plentiful. There was no lack of company now. The fields were gay as on the day before, yet they no longer set

Will watched the grand procession of a lady of rank

him rhyming—there was too much to see. Now a troop of recruits for the Spanish war marched by—boys taken from the plow, with here and there an older man who looked as if he knew the smell of powder. Now a squire on a goodly nag rode by. Merchants and artisans, yeomen and pedlars succeeded one another. And now there came toward him the train of some great lady, going from London to her country house.

Will had seen from a great distance the dust this grand procession raised. When it came up to him, he drew to the side of the road to watch. He could not marvel sufficiently at the showy display and at all it took, apparently, to clothe a lady of rank.

The coach her ladyship rode in was a huge affair with a great carved roof supported on four posts, each decorated atop with a streaming bunch of plumes and feathers—blue, red, and white. Will stared with all his might, for never before had he seen such a coach, it being a newly contrived vehicle.

But the lady within surpassed the coach in dusty grandeur. Will caught the sheen of a crimson velvet hooded cloak and the sparkle of gems. Her ladyship sat upon a bench lined with gaily colored cushions. And of these she seemed to have ample need; for, the body of the coach resting directly on the axles, she was kept bouncing continually up and down with the wheels. It was now well past noon. By this time her ladyship looked so worn that as her glance traveled casually to Will, her features conveyed no emotion save weariness. Behind her came twenty carts filled with trunks, boxes and hampers.

An old carrier who had stopped just behind Will to watch the procession clicked his tongue when all had gone by. "Eh, lad," he said with a disapproving shake of the head, "that's nowt to what I've seen. With the great farthingales that's in the fashion now, it do take a world o' stuff to fit a woman out. They be times! It's clothes, clothes, clothes. Maid, wife, or widow, all be the same. The country's gone stark ravin' mad, says I, for clothes—with ruffs and stom-achers and farthingales and great sleeves. 'Twas not so when I was a lad. And the men, they be worse than the women. There's many a young popinjay has sold the acres his father sweat to buy—and all to put grand clothes on his back. . . . But saw ye the face o' the woman? What part o' her a woman can change, she will—God gives 'em one face and they make themselves another!" And with a flick of his whip about the horse's rump, he drove on.

"What a sight it must be," said Will, riding alongside the cart, "when the Queen herself goeth a journey. I've heard it said she scorns to wear the same gown twice."

"In sooth, I know not," the old man replied. "I've ne'er laid eyes on the Queen myself, God save her! But when she goeth a journey to Greenwich out of London, they do say there's three hundred baggage loads follows her litter. Ay, they be times, they be times!"

"Think you we are like to meet with gentle-men-of-the-road?" Will asked to change the subject.

"With God's help we'll keep our purses," the carrier answered. "But an thou goest to London, thou wilt meet with a worse plague than highwaymen. When thou com'st nigh the city, thou'lt see as lusty a set of beggars as e'er swarmed at church door on Easter Day. A hefty staff's the only answer to 'em."

Will found the old man's words truly spoken when on the afternoon of the third day he neared London. Such crowds of beggars beset him that he had all he could do to make his way past them. One scarecrow after another seized hold of his horse's bridle. Dancing wildly about, the beggars demanded alms. At times Will found it difficult to keep his seat when some insistent fellow, refusing to take "Get thee gone!" for an answer, would swing on the bit and shout his excited horse into rearing. More than once Will found himself brandishing the short dagger he had thrust into his belt with little thought of using.

By late afternoon he was on the outskirts of London, abreast of the great gibbet at Tyburn. From the cross-beam dangled some twenty half-eaten corpses, which mercifully the flapping wings of crows almost hid from view.

"What were their crimes?" Will thought.

"Were they highwaymen? Murderers? Common thieves? I'll warrant more than one was hanged for the stealing of a sheep. And next month as many will die the death again. Ah me! Where such multitudes must beg, is it wonder that some will steal?"

For a little while after he had passed Tyburn, Will's spirits remained low. But presently the walled city rising before him took up all his thoughts. Now he found himself passing a whole succession of churches. Newgate, he had been told, was just beyond. He urged his tired horse forward, and with fast-beating heart rode through the gate into the city of his dreams.

3. "This Miracle, This London"

WILL's first care was to return his horse to the livery stable. But his progress through the crooked, narrow streets—most of them unpaved and thick with spring mud—was unbelievably slow.

He had heard of the busyness of London. Yet never in his busiest imagination had he conceived such traffic. Wherever the streets would bear them, thundering carts and coaches rumbled along, while in and out among them jostled such throngs of people that Will was afraid his horse would trample someone. Coming from the open country, he was at once struck by the dimness of the light. For the gabled, top-heavy houses overhung the streets. More than once he had to bend to avoid striking his head against a projecting upper story.

A fetid smell rose from the filthy gutters, into which all London's housewives cast their refuse. But nobody seemed to mind the stench except Will, whose nose was yet to become accustomed to it. Nor did anyone seem affected by the deafening noise, different in every street. In one the beating of hammers sounded. In another casks were being hooped. A third resounded to the clink of pots.

Will was grateful when he could dismount and give his horse into the keeping of the hostler. "Yet I am loth to part from the good beast," he said as he counted out the fee. "Three days and eighty miles have made us friends. But tell me if thou canst, which way I must go to find the Three Cranes. It hath been right heartily commended to me."

Having received directions, he threaded his way to Cheapside, found the inn by its red-latticed sign, and called for supper and a bed. He was eager to see more of the city. But it was late when supper was done. Besides, the other guests warned him of the danger of cutthroats after dark. So he sat down by the taproom fire to learn what he could of London from the talkative host.

"Ay, the streets be narrow and dark," the host admitted to Will's comment. "And getting darker all the time. Soon there'll not be air to breathe or light to see by."

"London's grown too big," put in the buxom hostess from her place behind the ale butt. "There's a hundred thousand folk within."

"And another hundred thousand without. Mind the hundred thousand outside the walls, Bess. They make up London, too. There's no town in England comes nigh London for size. Norwich is next, but Norwich numbers fifteen thousand. . . . Come you from far?" the host asked Will after a pause.

"If eighty miles be far."

"And what gale blows you to London?"

"Such wind," said Will, "as scatters young men through the world to seek their fortunes further than at home, where small experience grows."

"Well, you'll find plenty o' your own sort in the taverns—London draws young men as honey doth the bee. Some o' them work, some drink and waste, some starve. 'Tis no easy thing to make your way in London with a purse that's lean. Victual's high. What do we give for butter now, Bess?"

"A penny the pound," the hostess returned promptly. "And cream's a shilling and sixpence the gallon. Eggs a halfpenny each."

"There, now. Victual's high. I gave a shilling for that pig ye eat of. And for a sheep 'tis six shillings we give."

Will found his mind wandering from the

figures. Pleading weariness, he went to his room. But it was long before he lay down. Opening the latticed window, he stood leaning out, gazing into the dim-lit street, letting the strange night noises mingle with his excited thoughts.

Next morning he was early afoot. "I'll not seek employment today," he said to himself. "One single day I'll give over to viewing this miracle, this London, this leviathan that tomorrow swallows me up."

He went out into the already busy street. With a twelve-hour workday before them, Londoners, he found, had got an early start. At the corners he had to push his way through crowds of women, girls, and apprentices, who, armed with great buckets and pitchers, stood chatting and laughing as they waited their turn at the pump. From upstairs windows, slops were being emptied into the gutters. The shops and stalls had opened at seven, and as Will walked along he was beset on all sides with invitations to buy. Above the rattle of wooden wheels rose a constant din of tradesmen's cries: "New

brooms, green brooms!" "Hot peas!" "Oatcake
—hot, fine oatcake!" "Whiting, whiting!"
"Rock samphire!" "What do ye lack? What do
ye lack?" "Buy a mat!" "What do ye lack?"

Smiling at the thought of all he lacked, Will
bought a piece of oatcake and ate it as he went
along. He was making his way toward St. Paul's
Cathedral, which—in spite of the fact that its
steeple had burnt down—was still the highest
point in sight. It was not the church itself that
drew him. He knew that for the price of a
penny he could climb to the steeple's base and
get a bird's-eye view of London.

With this in mind he approached the cathedral. But he stood transfixed with amazement
when he stepped inside. There was none of the
quiet sanctity he had expected—no whispering
shadows, no air of soft expectancy. A hubbub
as of a market place filled the cathedral. Indeed, he quickly saw that the middle aisle of
the nave was a veritable market. Ale, bacon,
bread, fish, fruit, and meat were loudly being
cried for sale. And nothing in the manner of

buyers or sellers suggested that they were in a place of worship.

Will Shakespeare stared about him in utmost astonishment while his ears took in the mixture of voices and footsteps that made up the general hum. Small knots of men stood talking here and there, others walked about alone, reading the placards and advertisements of help wanted that were affixed to nearly every pillar. Will did not know St. Paul's was the great news exchange of London. But he quickly caught on to the fact that every variety of man came here —to talk, to do business, to pick up easy money, to read the advertisements, to gape.

" 'Tis a map of London," he said to himself as he noted with excitement the different trades, professions, and types around him. He saw tailors waiting, tape measure in hand, for customers; lawyers discussing their cases; knights and army captains clanking their long rapiers; moneylenders offering to save merchants from bankruptcy. Many types Will did not yet know. But already he had enough experience of life to pick out the scholar, the gallant, the gentleman, the upstart, the beggar, the cut-purse.

Though it shocked him, the sight fascinated him, too. He could have lingered there indefinitely. But remembering that he was to give but a single day to seeing London, Will paid his penny and clambered to the roof.

4. *From the Roof of St. Paul's*

LONDON with its hundred spires lay sprawled beneath him. He scarcely saw it at first. His eye went straight to the river that embraced the city on the south side.

"Ah," thought he, feasting his eyes on the Thames and its thousands of boats that plied up the river, down the river, and across from shore to shore, "this is the glory of the city. This is London's great thoroughfare—and not any wonder that, seeing the streets are well nigh impassable."

Here and there amid the traffic of small wherries carrying passengers and freight, his eye picked out royal barges, gay with banners. But no sea-going vessels were among them. Far to the left, London Bridge with its twenty proud arches spanned the river. Farther down he could see a mass of ships lying at their moorings. "Merchants' argosies," thought Will, "coming who knows from what distant shores, out of what stormy adventures. Below must lie Drake's *Golden Hind* that took him all around the world."

Now Will's eye traveled to the opposite shore. He did not know this was Southwark. But he easily recognized the circular building there as the Bear Garden, where the popular sport of setting dogs to fight a bear went on. He passed over it with little interest. Indeed, the whole of Southwark took but a moment of his time. For how could he guess that one day his thoughts and all his hopes, his triumphs and his loves would be centered on a structure there that would forever be coupled with his name?

From the river Will turned his eyes to the Tower of London. Standing squarely on the

Thames below the bridge, the Tower's bulk loomed gloomy and impressive. He looked long and feelingly upon it. For not only was this the most famous building in England. Something

From the roof of St. Paul's, Will gazed out at London

in himself answered to the drama that for so many centuries had been enacted there.

His blood quickened at thought of the noble captives — offenders most dangerous to the crown—who had passed through those grim portals. How many had left the Tower only for the execution block! How many had never left it at all, being foully murdered there! "What tales those walls could tell!" thought Will. And again his eye passed to the far end of London Bridge where all knew the grisly heads of thirty traitors were exposed to view.

No other structure in the city held him as did the Tower. He merely glanced at the splendid palaces that lined the Strand along the river bank. The rest of the city he scanned quickly, marveling more at its size than anything else. Then with his back to the Thames he looked beyond the battlemented wall to the northeast.

Far off across the fields two circular turrets stood out. On these Will's eyes fixed themselves intently. For these two landmarks were the objects of his journey, the end and goal of all his present hopes. One was the Theater, where

Richard Burbage played. The other was the Curtain, but who played there he did not know.

"Tomorrow I shall try my fortune," Will said to himself.

He climbed down and, leaving St. Paul's, gave himself over to the magic of the city. All day he wandered about. By dusk he had drunk in a thousand new impressions and could take in no more. He found his way back to the Three Cranes, ate his supper, and at once dropped into a heavy, dreamless sleep.

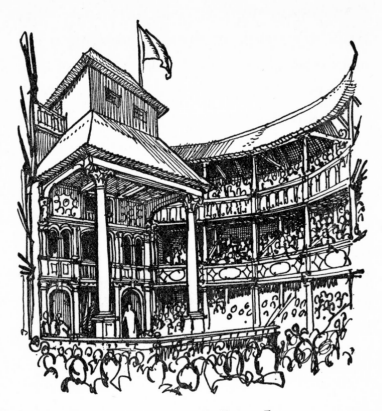

5. *A Setback*

THE person on whom Will Shakespeare relied to help him get on the stage was James Burbage, actor and owner of the Theater. No man in London was more passionately devoted to the art. Will thought himself in love with make-believe. But even Will himself would have admitted that his feeling was a twig compared with the enduring trunk of Burbage's devotion.

James Burbage had trudged the roads of England. His feet knew well the feel of gravel in his boots. His shoulders had bowed many a time to the weight of a showman's cart stuck in the mud. The tedious toil of packing and unpacking theatrical properties and costumes, the labor of setting and resetting boards on trestles, the indifferent food of the wayside, the doubtful beds of inns—all the hardships of a trouper were as familiar to him as the faces of his companions.

He had done with all of it now. Ten years ago he had built the first theater in England— for he had been a carpenter before he was an actor—and now with a father's natural pride he watched his son Richard win the applause of London on his own stage.

In building his theater James Burbage had taken the inn-yards, in which he had acted so long, for a model. What he built was an inn-yard without the inn around it. But instead of making it a rectangle, he built his theater round, like the circular bear pit. "The see-ing's better," he was wont to say. "Better yet, the walls give back the voice as the inns can-not. The voice, say I, the voice is the important thing. I would not give a pippin for a dumb-show."

To James Burbage, who felt that a play was more to be heard than seen, the circular theater was a triumph of invention. He built tiers of galleries all around the walls. The stage he made jutted halfway into the pit. There the actors would get the full light of the open sky —the theater having no roof except a fringe of thatch over the spectators' seats—and their voices would be heard as though they stood in the very center of a well.

It was to this proud theater beyond the city walls that Will Shakespeare directed his steps on his third afternoon in London. There was no missing the building. For the flag flying from its turret to announce there would be a play that day could be seen from a great dis-tance. Besides, as he came near, he realized that others were theater-bound as well. Groups of

men and women who had come out of the
suburbs were streaming across Finsbury Fields.
Many stopped short of his destination and entered the Curtain. But Will went on. His plan
was to see the play, then go backstage to the
tiring rooms and get a word with James Burbage. In the pocket of his doublet was a letter
which he meant to use as a last resort to get a
hearing.

Handing his penny to the gatherer at the
door, Will found himself at once admitted to
the pit. There were no seats here. But like the
apprentices around him, he had no money to
waste on comfort. Besides, he wanted to be as
near the stage as possible. Richard Burbage was
going to appear in one of his most celebrated
roles—as Hieronimo in *The Spanish Tragedy*
—and Will didn't want to lose a gesture or a
word. Moreover, soon he himself would be
treading those boards, perhaps, and he wanted
to note every detail of the stage.

Much of this he could do while waiting,
there being no curtain to shut the stage from
view. Only at the back were there curtains—

three sets, one above the other. And Will guessed easily what lay beyond each.

Hidden behind those on the stage level must be the inner stage. In the coming play it would represent a room in a house, the banquet hall of a castle, a throne room, a cave, or even a tomb chamber, perhaps. The curtains just above would doubtless disclose a balcony, or an upstairs room, or a battlement. And behind the top set of curtains the musicians and trumpeters must even now be getting their instruments ready.

For the theater had rapidly filled. A number of richly dressed young gentlemen had even climbed on the stage itself and were sitting on stools along either side. Some of these dandies had begun to smoke pipes. Others had bought fruit and drinks from the vendors. One was busily cracking walnuts and flicking the shells into the pit, much to the annoyance of the groundlings.

But now a flourish of trumpets announced that the play was about to begin. The noise died down. With a sense that he was about to

Will stood entranced in the pit of the Theater

lose touch with the earth, Will fixed his eyes on
the entrance and exit doors.

Afterwards, when he had begun to struggle
with the writing of plays, Will often recalled
the thrills and sensations of this first play with
its blood, its revenge, its ghosts, and its horrors.
Line after line of the speeches stayed vividly
in his mind. But when on this afternoon the
stage had been cleared and the audience had

begun to pile out, his thoughts jumped at once
to his own affairs. He climbed on the stage and,
passing through an exit, found himself in the
tiring room.

Most of the players were already putting on
their proper clothes. But Richard Burbage,
whose powerful role had clearly taken everything out of him, sat drooping on a clothes
chest and swabbing at his brow. An older man
with a short, square beard meantime pressed
a tankard of ale into his other hand.

"Master Burbage, sir . . ." Will said softly,
doffing his hat and bowing.

Both men looked up. "Which of us do you
address?" the older man asked. He eyed the
intruder sharply, but was at once disarmed by
Will's gentle face and well-bred manner.

"Either or both, if it please you," said Will
and bowed once more. "Sirs, I will not weary
you with circumlocution. My name is Shakespeare. I am but newly come to London, having
had some experience of the private stage, and
I would fain be of your company, than which,"

he added with a spurt of admiration, "there can be none more excellent."

James Burbage smiled at Will's fervor. " 'Tis clear," he said, not unkindly, "that you are but newly come. London runneth over with players. There be more players in't than there be parts. 'Tis plays we need, not players, for ever the cry's for something new. We are well measured to our needs."

"Do you then never hire a player from outside?" asked Will with a sinking heart.

"Only when some particular play calls for more parts than we by doubling can make up. And then the hired man must be one skilled at quick attiring. For he must play half a dozen different parts. I advise, unless you be excellent in the quality we players profess, to return to the province whence you came."

"Sir," said Will, grasping for time, "I dare not speak of my excellence that have seen Richard Burbage play Hieronimo. But I have here a letter of commendation from Sir Thomas Hesketh of Rufford. I was some

" 'Tis plays we need, not players," said James Burbage

months a player in his household. Ere that I was two years with Squire Houghton of Lea."

James Burbage glanced through the letter Will put in his hands. "That which will do excellently well in a gentleman's household is like to do but ill in London," he said, returning it. "Can you fence?"

"I have not the skill of weapons."

"Can you dance the galliard, do the capriole, the volte?"

"Sir, I know not what the terms signify."

"Can you leap from a twelve-foot tower?"

"I am strong-knit, Master Burbage, as you can see, but I have not been a tumbler, sir."

"Can you play on the lute, the cittern, the bandore?"

"Music, sir, I know but indifferently well."

"Then so far as I can see," said Burbage, "you have but two things a player needs—your speaking voice is rich and deep, and your words flow trippingly on your tongue. 'Tis not enough. I say to you again, go home."

Will's heart had sunk lower and lower with each question the old theater owner put to him.

But at the words "go home" something inside him tightened. "That I cannot do," he said firmly. "I thank you, Master Burbage, for your time and your advice which I am sure is kindly meant, but I will not retreat."

"In that case, Father," Richard Burbage spoke up, "do not you discourage him out of measure. The Curtain, Master Shakespeare, can give you no employment. That we know, having an interest in it. But if you are so set on being a player as you say, go to the companies that play in the inns. The Admiral's Men, of whom young Edward Alleyn is one, may find a small part for you. Or try Lord Strange's Men. You may not have all that London demands of a player, but the will's somewhat. If I have any skill at reading faces, we'll yet hear of you."

Will Shakespeare left the Theater in a hurly-burly of emotions. But, for all that his hopes were dashed, he was not cast down. "I will strive with things impossible," he said to himself as he trudged back. "Yea, and overcome them, too!"

6. *Gaining a Foothold*

IN HIS attic room, meanly furnished and un-
heated, Will Shakespeare sat bowed over
his table writing. A single candle, now
burnt down to within an inch of the candle-
stick, threw a dim, unsteady light on the papers
before him and cast his exaggerated shadow on
the paneled wall. The goose quill in his hand
moved with practised ease. Now and again it

45

paused midway in a line. Often it stopped altogether while Will's eyes traveled to an open
playbook propped up in front of him. Outside,
a cold spring rain drove against the leaded
panes. But Will was unaware of the rain. He
was absorbed in his work and as lost to the
weather as he was indifferent to the chill of the
room. . . . Will Shakespeare was writing his
first play.

Four years had passed since James and Richard Burbage had so differently advised him.
In those four years Will had gone a long way.
No longer did he have to plead with managers
to give him a chance. On a dozen different
stages he had proved his ability. All the great
inns of London knew him. He had played at
both the Theater and the Curtain. Now he
was engaged at the Rose, the new theater which
Philip Henslowe—a man with an eye to a good
investment—had put up across the Thames.
Young Edward Alleyn was bringing in the
crowds there. True, Will was not a regular
member of the Admiral's company. Nor did
he belong to any of the other companies that

Will Shakespeare was writing his first play

played under the protection of great lords.
He was still a "hired man." But he was re-
spected as such.

The four years behind him had been the
hardest, yet the most wonderful, Will had
known. They had been so crowded with work
and study, so filled to the brim and flowing
over with things learned from the streets and
houses of London, from stage, tiring room and
playbooks, that the years had passed like so
many months.

Will smiled sometimes when he thought of

the lowly work he had done to gain a foothold on the stage. His days as call boy, when he had never stepped on the stage at all except to help move some heavy property, were the worst to remember. "For then," Will used to say, "I was like one athirst who held the cup for another and ne'er sipped a drop himself." Then his first bit part, got by chance when a hired man failed to appear; the astonishment at his knowing the lines—which was really no mystery at all since he managed always to be around at rehearsals; the still greater amazement at his good performance; the praise of Ned Alleyn himself.

That afternoon was a thing apart in Will's memory. It was the seed from which all else had sprung. For now that he had proved he could "fill in," he had been called on whenever the company was short. He had helped the players out of many a tight spot.

Then once in his gentle, well-bred way he had suggested a different wording for some lines. Quietly he had pointed out ways to cut the script and patch it so the cuts wouldn't show. On his own initiative he had expanded a couple of speeches—with such magical effect that Ned Alleyn had been lavish in his praise. After that it was continually, "Rework this, cut that, expand the other." In little, lowly ways he had become indispensable.

And now for the first time Will was trying to soar. He had got hold of an old play about King Henry VI, Joan of Arc, and the siege of Orleans. Three of the university wits had thrown it together for the Admiral's Men. But the play had not "taken" and wasn't being used any more. "Yet the times are ripe for such a play," thought Will. "Since the Armada and Spain's defeat, London hath shouted itself hoarse with patriotism. Any play that repeats the glories of our past should win the plaudits of the multitude. If I can but make this brave, dead Talbot live again!"

He would have to write some roaring speeches for this "terror of the French"— London was mad for high-flown speeches. One would have thought words were newly invented, the way people hungered for them.

They couldn't get enough of words, it seemed;
they were amused by every twist and play on
sound, they jumped to the meaning of every
pun. And poetry went to their heads like wine.
Time and again he had seen them lifted out
of themselves and carried away—as he himself
had been—by Marlowe's *Tamburlaine*.

When Will left Stratford on that bright
spring day four years before, he had been full
of misgivings about the university wits who
wrote the plays. How would he rate among
those clever, learned young men? He was un-
taught, unpractised. He laughed now when he
remembered his fears. There was but one
among them all whom he regarded with awe,
and that was Christopher Marlowe. From the
rest he had learned something here and there.
But they were too slapdash about their work
to teach him much. Seldom did one of them
take the time to write a play alone—the players
were in too great a hurry for their play. To
get it done fast, two or three men as a rule
would work together. Sometimes a whole crew

joined forces. One would supply the plot, the others would each write an act. They would get the whole thing done in an astounding hurry, sell it, then turn their minds to some other hack work to get them out of debt. Their play-making wasn't art, and they knew it. They wrote plays for money. Their best talents they kept to throw into the careful verse they wrote for love.

But Christopher Marlowe was different. Kit Marlowe wrote plays that *were* great poetry. "There's one whom any man might call his master and be proud," Will thought. He could not praise *Tamburlaine* enough. Marlowe had sprinkled his play thick with the thrills and sensations the audience demanded. But that was not what Will admired. He admired the *suspense* of the play, and he admired its wonderful lines.

"Ah, Kit Marlowe is a Colossus," he thought, "and we petty men must be content to walk between his huge legs. . . ."

The candle on Will's table had burned

nearly to the end. He laid his pen down, blew out the sputtering flame, and undressed in the dark.

" 'Tis but patching and botching I've done," he said with a sigh as he pulled the covers over him. "But still—I know not how 'tis—I feel myself on the edge of things boundless, as if I were embarked upon the vasty deep. Ahead all is uncharted. I know not whither I am bound, but only what I seek."

7. *Johnny-Do-All*

WILL SHAKESPEARE often dreamed at
night of meeting Kit Marlowe and
telling him how much he was admired. But in his waking moments Will knew
it was not likely that he and Marlowe should
ever meet. "We belong to different worlds. Of
themselves our paths will never cross. Yet meet
him I shall," thought Will. "When I have writ
some worthy thing, I'll seek him out. Then I

shall say to him, 'This, this, and this I have learned from you.' "

How soon that would be, he dared not guess. There was so little time for writing! Back in Stratford he had been dazzled by the glamor of the stage. But in London he had soon learned that a player's life was an ounce of glamor to a pound of work. The spectators' cry for something new kept the players going at a terrific pace. Every day in the week they had to put on a different play. If something proved popular, they might repeat it after a week perhaps. But only as good a play as *The Spanish Tragedy* or *Tamburlaine* would see the boards twenty times in a season.

Will found every hour of his day accounted for. In the morning it was rehearsal; in the afternoon, performance; in the evening, learning his new part. The night alone was left for writing. And so often it could not be his own. So often there was this to patch and that to cut and the other to expand for the morrow. It was all he could do to keep up with the day's demands. "And yet people suppose a player's life is naught but cakes and ale," Will thought wryly. "There's not an apprentice in leathern apron that works as hard as we players do."

Not that he minded work. Will had no yearning for London's pleasures. Cockfighting and bearbaiting were not for him. The wine shop and the tavern did not beckon him. He liked his work routine, he liked the dignity of regular pay, he liked owing nothing to any man. And he often marveled at the disordered life most of the play-makers chose to live. They quarreled and fought, they drank too heavily and swore too much. When they had money, they wasted it scandalously. When they had none, they borrowed or starved. In and out of debt, in and out of prison, in and out of one scrape after another—that was their fashion.

It was not Will's way. He came from a good home, of a good family. His manners reflected it and his habits lived up to it. He had no debts and he had no quarrels.

It was thus no small surprise to him when one day after rehearsal Ned Alleyn called him over and said, "Will, I see you have an enemy—

or had, for he's dead now these three weeks."

"And who might that be?" Will asked smiling, for he thought Ned Alleyn was jesting.

"Greene. You knew him—Robert Greene, that drinking, brawling, red-headed fellow who writ so many plays for us. Here's a book of his, out yesterday. There's a letter in't to his friends. Greene says he's sorry that e'er he made plays for us. He calls us apes and puppets who can speak only the words the play-makers put in our mouths. He bids his friends write no more plays for us because, forsooth, 'those rude grooms,' he says, 'will throw you over in the end—as they have me.' "

"But what has't to do with me?" asked Will. "Wherein have I offended him?"

"Why, see you not? You have trespassed, Will. You have poached on their ground—made plays for us. So he can't speak ill enough o' you. He calls you a crow beautified with their feathers. He says you suppose you can write verse as well as the best of them. You're a Johnny-do-all, he says, and think yourself the only Shake-scene in the country."

Will flushed. " 'Tis true I'm a Johnny-do-all," he said. "But I have given no man cause to say I am conceited. Nor that I hold myself above the play-makers. While Marlowe lives——"

"Faith, man, start not on Marlowe again, for I must home to dinner. . . . Nay, Will, defend not thyself to me. 'Tis all Greene's venom, all venom and gall. Those rhymesters can't forgive us for earning more than they do. They envy us our satin suits."

Though Will laughed, it was a long time before he forgot the matter. Greene's ugly words kept paining him. But they did not stop him from writing. More than ever he turned to play-making. He stole time from sleep. He stole time from friendship.

Already he had a number of plays to his credit. He had written two more about King Henry VI. Then he had written a play he called *Titus Andronicus.* It was not a good play, and Will knew it, but it was full of the blood and horrors that London audiences loved and had become so popular that three different companies played it. Then Will had tried his hand at some light comedies in the Italian manner.

Now he began working on another kind of play. Some time before, he had got hold of a history book. There was a character in it that fascinated Will much more than Henry VI had done. It was Richard III, the crippled king whose soul was as crooked as his body. "This is just the sort of hero that would appeal to Marlowe," Will thought. "An evil man who is mad for power and wades through blood to get it. I can make a better play of it than any I've done. It will be a better play than any I've played in. This one I can show to Marlowe."

He plunged into it with enthusiasm. But he had not got through the second act when something threw his mind in an altogether different direction.

8. *While the Plague Raged*

THE plague had come.

The dreaded plague was always paying a visit to filthy, undrained, rat-ridden London. But this time it had taken the city over. Day by day the deaths mounted. And now so many were dying that the London Council took steps. People must be stopped from congregating, for wherever there were crowds the infection spread. Let the play-houses be closed!

That was the end of play-making. For what was the use of writing a play when it couldn't be sold or acted? With the playhouses shut down, the players were going off to tour the provinces. They wouldn't do new things there. They were taking along only the old, well-tried plays that had been successes. *Richard III* might sleep in a drawer till better times came— there was no hurry about him now.

Will considered what he should do. Ned Alleyn was joining Lord Strange's Men and going on tour with them. Will Kempe, the best clown in London, was going along with him. John Heminges, of whom Will was very fond, was also to be of the company. But there was no place for him. The company was cut to the bone and only three other players were going along. The same was true of all the other companies. They stripped themselves not only of every costume and property they could do without, but also of every actor they could spare. Will's greatest value was as a Johnny-do-all. He wasn't needed now.

"I shall stay in London and wait till the playhouses open," Will decided. "The plague will not stay forever. In a few months everything will be as before."

He told this to his friends. But he said nothing of the idea that was joggling around in the back of his head.

As far back as his grammar school days, Will had written songs and poems. They were little things—a dozen lines here, twenty lines there. It had never occurred to him to get any of them into print. They were just something he did for the joy of the doing—because he loved putting words together, because he took delight in pattern and lilt and rhyme.

But browsing around the bookstalls in St. Paul's Churchyard in his rare free hours, Will had picked up many a book of poems. For in London every writer's ambition was to live with fame and write for fame. And poetry could assure a man that as nothing else could.

Will picked up many a book of poems in the bookstalls

Plays? Plays, the writers thought, were something you wrote for the common mob. Plays were something you did just to pay the bills. Plays would never bring a man fame. Half the time the ones that got into print didn't even bear the writer's name. When you sold a play to a company, you lost all right to it. You couldn't control what got into print. If a play became popular, the company might sell it to a printer. Then it would come out all chopped and mangled so you would hardly recognize it as your own. Or perhaps some spectator would steal the play. There were plenty of pirates in London who sat in the galleries and took down all they could of a popular play. What they missed they made up from memory. And what a jumble they made of it! When you read the lines, you were glad your name wasn't on the title page. What fame was there in stuff like that?

Will noticed that every book he bought was dedicated to some great lord. It was the custom, and Will could easily understand why it prevailed. As a rule the poets were poor men who needed a patron to help them. It was hard to make a living out of writing. If you dedicated a book to an important person, he would make you a gift of money, or get you some easy post at court, or give you board and room in his house, or let you tutor his son perhaps. Besides, the patron would show the book to all his fine acquaintance. They in turn would buy it. And, of course, such people were the very ones to appreciate a well-turned phrase. When you were after fame, a good patron was almost as important as a good poem.

Now Will had become acquainted with some of the rich young men who sat upon the stage to watch the plays. They liked his acting, they liked his gentle manners, and they were interested in him because he was the only actor in London who wrote plays. When Greene attacked Will, several of these young gentlemen had gone to the printer and got him to print an apology. And among these was a young man of very great family—Henry Wriothesley, Earl of Southampton and Baron of Tichfield. He was just nineteen years old and he had one of the most enormous fortunes in England.

Will Shakespeare decided that he, too,

wanted fame. He would write a poem and dedicate it to the Earl of Southampton.

"I have money laid by," Will said to himself. "I shall not starve. And do not I owe myself a holiday? How pleasant 'twill be to sit all day unhurried and choose the one word of all words that is right for the sound and the sense and the measure! 'Tis a happiness not to be missed. For once the playhouses open, I shall scarce have an hour to call mine own."

The same day that the players bade Will farewell, he began working on his poem. It was to be about Venus and her love for the beautiful youth Adonis, who would be killed by a wild boar. The story was not his own. But that never bothered Will. He was content to take his plots wherever he found them.

"And this one," he thought, "is just such a one as will appeal to a very much courted young man with a university education. . . . But how amazing this is!" he said to himself as his quill raced over the page. "The rhymes come of themselves. 'Tis as though I had dreamt it all and needed but to set it down. This is holiday indeed!"

Pure holiday it would have been if Will had never needed to go out. But as soon as he was in the street, the grief and terror of plague-stricken London gripped him. He was not afraid for himself. He had been born in a plague year and felt somehow that that protected him. But who could hear the almost constant tolling of the bells and not be moved? People no longer asked for whom the death knell clanged. "Good men's lives expire before the flowers in their caps," thought Will. "They die ere they sicken."

"Smoke a pipe, Master Shakespeare, an ye mean to go out," Will's landlady advised him. " 'Twill keep ye from th' infection. Or chew a bit o' the peel o' th' orange. 'Tis near as good. And mind, Master Shakespeare, that ye walk in the middle o' the street. There's the quarantine two doors down and a watch set night and day to keep them that live in the house from coming out. But I warrant some o' them'll get out anyhow. 'Tis long to be shut up twenty days."

When Will was in the streets, London and the plague seemed very real. But as soon as he returned to his room, the troubled city fell from him as though it didn't exist. He flung himself with delight into each new stanza and left it with the same feeling of satisfaction. It seemed to him the poem was writing itself and that he was merely holding the quill.

In a few weeks *Venus and Adonis* was done. Will took it to the printer, then came home and got *Richard III* out of the drawer. The poem had been too easy to do. He needed something that made him reach to get it. Besides, his mind was running on Marlowe. Now that Will had time he wanted to seek out his idol—but not with empty hands. He began to work furiously on the play.

He had all but finished it when news came that Christopher Marlowe had been stabbed in a tavern. He had died on the spot.

9. "We Want You with Us"

THE Earl of Southampton was delighted to be William Shakespeare's patron. For no sooner was *Venus and Adonis* put out for sale in the spring of 1593 than every copy was snatched up. Everyone was enchanted with the poem. Printing after printing poured from the press. "Mellifluous!" people said. "O dulcet singer! O honey-tongued Shakespeare! What an enchanting quill he hath!"

There was no question in the Earl's mind

what, under these circumstances, he should do. William Shakespeare must lodge at his palace, write more poems, and dedicate them all to the Earl of Southampton, Baron of Tichfield. The young nobleman had been brought up by Lord Burghley, Queen Elizabeth's Lord High Treasurer, and was supposed to marry his granddaughter. But marriage was far from Henry Wriothesley's mind. He was not yet twenty. He was fabulously wealthy. And for the time he wanted to be free. He lived surrounded by rich, carefree, adventurous young men as light-hearted as himself. How much it would add to their talk to have the author of *Venus and Adonis* in their midst!

An invitation from the Earl of Southampton was as good as a summons—Will couldn't refuse. Nor did he want to. He was ever ready for a new experience of men and things. And he was curious to see what the plumed and perfumed young dandies who sat upon the stage were like on their own home ground. So he willingly became a part of the Earl's sumptuous household and used his eyes and ears to their full extent.

It was a different and, for a time, a more exciting life than any Will had ever dreamed of living. But once the newness had worn off, it palled on him. He longed to be back in the theater. This world of wealth and splendor and careless gaiety was not his own. He was a craftsman and he missed his craft. It was not enough that he was writing another poem—poetry in itself no longer gripped him, it merely amused him. He missed the hard-working people of the theater. He missed the joy of creating something together.

He knew now what would give him satisfaction. Poetry such as he was writing might be "mellifluous," honey-sweet, but it was too narrow—it cramped his thoughts and his feelings. It gave him no chance to express the deeper things that filled his heart and mind. And he thought, "Poems may be right for others, but only a play is right for me. Only into a play can I pour all I have learned of men and women and life."

It was with a sense of relief that Will finished his poem. He dedicated it to the Earl of Southampton, and then, as gracefully as he could, left the house. He had taken from it all that he wanted. He had twenty, thirty, forty characters he could put into plays. He knew exactly how rich young men lived, talked, loved, jested, looked at life. As for the soft bed, the luxurious food, the attendance on every hand—he did not need them and did not want them. He would give all for a morning's stiff rehearsal.

With a lighter heart than he had had any time in the two years of the plague, Will walked east through London. "I feel free again," he thought. "And how pat everything falls! The plague is fast lifting, the theaters will open soon, the players will be back in town. It may be some are here already."

With that he turned up Bread Street and pushed open the door of the Mermaid Tavern, which the players frequented.

"Will Shakespeare!"

A lump came into Will's throat as, looking

through the smoke haze that filled the room, he saw a group of his old comrades from various companies sitting together at a table. James Burbage seemed to be presiding. Kempe was on his right, John Heminges on his left. Augustine Phillips, William Sly, Thomas Pope, and Henry Condell were ranged on either side of the table, while Richard Burbage sat at the foot. There was no mistaking the pleasure in their faces at sight of him. There was no doubting the warmth of their greetings.

"The very man we want to see," James Burbage said when Will, having shaken hands with all, sat down by Heminges. "We knew not where to find you."

Will looked with pleased surprise from one to another of the group. For it seemed to him a strange assembly. He knew that three years before these same men had quarreled with Burbage and left the Theater to go with Ned Alleyn to the Rose.

"Be not so amazed, Will," Richard Burbage said. "We're friends again and all's forgot. Behold! You see before you the Lord Chamberlain's Men! We've reorganized. Others whom you know well will shortly be of our company."

"And Ned Alleyn?" asked Will. "What of him?"

"Ah, Ned Alleyn is tied to Henslowe," John Heminges said. "Now that he has married Henslowe's daughter, 'tis natural he must stick with the Rose."

"Richard will be our lead," said James Burbage, glancing proudly at his son. "We have no need of Alleyn. I'll put it to you plain, Will. We want you with us."

"Aye!" came from several of the rest.

"With all my heart," said Will, his face red with joy. "There are no players in London I hold more high, nor any I'd rather work with— or make plays for."

"Then you'll be a sharer like the rest—buy your way in and take the gains and the losses as they come. Art content?"

"Content and more!" cried Will. "Boy, fetch us canary! And cups for all! This calls for wine, my friends. I call not to mind a happier hour."

"Will," said Henry Condell, "you've took London by storm. We heard your name all the way from Bath. How doth the ivy sit upon your brow?"

"A plague on fame, Harry!" cried Will. "The play's the thing! And, friends, I have one you can open with."

"Is't a comedy?" asked Kempe.

"Nay, Will, 'tis a tragedy."

"Another *Titus Andronicus?*"

He found a group of old friends in the Mermaid Tavern

"I think 'tis better. Richard, the hero's thy namesake, Richard III."

"Then shall we drink to him?" asked Kempe.

"Nay," said Richard. "Drink rather to William the Conqueror here!"

"Let us drink," said Will, raising his cup amidst the laughter, "to the Lord Chamberlain's Men. May they ever hold fast together!"

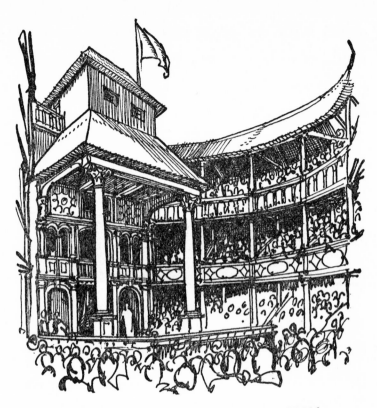

10. *Will Sizes Up His Company*

FTER that meeting at the Mermaid, Will walked on air—his vagabond days were over. No longer would he be a hired man, shifting about from company to company, sometimes employed and sometimes not.

He would be a sharer, he would *belong*. Together with ten or at most a dozen men he would own the company's properties, costumes, playbooks. The years of a shilling a day for hired man's pay were done forever.

"To be sure," Will said to himself, his head in the clouds, "I'll have to take the losses as well as the gains. But with such a company as these my fellows, with such a manager as James Burbage, losses may well-nigh be dismissed."

A wonderful sense of sureness possessed him as he entered the Theater on the morning of the first rehearsal. A dozen plays had to be got ready at once for the opening weeks, and the excitement of coming back to the London stage infected everyone. Yet all fell at once into their parts. And as they did so, Will studied each player—his voice, his walk, his build, his gestures—judged the power of his acting and guessed how far each player might go. From now on these men would play the characters he created. Everything he wanted to say must be said through them. On them

would depend whether or not the vision in his
mind got across to the audience. "I must know
my instruments," he thought, "that I may get
from each all that it is capable of sounding. I
must not ask more, nor will I aim at less, than
all that a man can give."

As he watched, sitting by John Heminges,
waiting for their scene, Will's excitement and
satisfaction grew. "We have many faults," he
admitted to himself, "but none that cannot be
corrected. Richard is excellent! He is better
far than Alleyn. Ned struts and postures. He
rants, he uses too much force—he o'ersteps the
modesty of nature. And he will not be lessoned.
But Richard! Ah, what things Richard and I
will do together! Yea, and all our company.
For none here is stiff-necked—unless it be Will
Kempe, perchance."

With special pleasure he watched the boys
who would play his women's parts. One was a
little lad, not more than twelve years old,
Will guessed. "He's my apprentice," John
Heminges whispered proudly. "A lad 'tis a joy
to teach. See how he manages his hands and

During rehearsals Will studied each player carefully

feet. Will, I've fourteen children of my own. But I swear not one's his equal. My Rebecca mothers him more than all the rest, I do believe."

"And whose is the handsome tall lad?"

"Richard's apprentice. A good boy, too," Heminges said. "Graceful as a willow wand."

"Those two are charming," thought Will. "Would they not look wondrous well as mistress and maid? And how that tall one would carry it off if I disguised him as a youth!"

When the rehearsal was over, Will stayed behind. He wanted to go over all the theater and poke his nose into all the places he had never visited before. He clambered even to the turret above the stage. He had used that turret in Henry VI—his Joan of Arc had ascended to its very top to thrust out a flaming torch. Now he went inside the huts and examined the pulleys by means of which gods and winged spirits could descend from above. This was the place of storms and battles, too. A great metal box with bullets ready to be rolled to make artillery noise stood there. Will took one up curiously—he had used its effects already. Then lightly he sounded the great drum that made the boom of thunder.

Coming down, he put his head in at the door of the costume room. But he didn't go in. The company's costumes would be sufficiently rich and grand, he knew. For this was one place where make-believe stopped being make-believe. The full light of day fell on the stage, spectators stood within hand's reach all around, and richly dressed gallants sat upon the stage itself. Only costumes of real velvet, satin, cloth of gold, and silver lace would give a sense of reality to the play.

The brilliant cloaks and doublets he saw hanging on the pegs doubtless were not so grand as the least of Ned Alleyn's costumes. Will knew Ned didn't count the cost when he needed something fine—he had spent a fortune on a single velvet cloak with cape embroidered in gold, garnets, and pearls. But the costumes of the Lord Chamberlain's Men would be grand enough. With all England mad for clothes, and fashions changing all the time, discarded

Will was curious to see what the property room held

clothes could always be bought. And since the audience didn't require the costumes to suit the place and time of the play, there was no problem. Splendor was all that was necessary, and splendor there would be.

Will was far more curious to see what the property room held, though he knew, more or less, what he might expect to find. For every company must have on hand properties to make real the scenes of torture and bloodshed the public craved. Whips for floggings, an execution block, a gallows, axes, bows and arrows, tombs—yes, here were the bleeding heads and hands that his own *Titus Andronicus* had called for. An assortment of arms and legs to be chopped off lay piled in a corner. A lion and two lion's heads took up another. A snake, dragons, a chariot, a bed, two thrones, a basin, a shepherd's crook, tankards, torches— there was much that would be useful here. The bed and one of the tombs would do for the *Romeo and Juliet* he had begun to write. He'd need a rope ladder, though, a spade, a lantern, and a crowbar.

It never occurred to Will to be troubled by the fact that except for such properties his stage would be bare. He knew his audience. He trusted their imagination. The spectators, he was confident, would piece out the imperfections with their thoughts. "If our art be true," he told himself, "it can change those two posts into a forest, or turn this bare scaffold into the war-wasted fields of France. We can make the spectators believe the sun's glare is moonlight sleeping on a bank, and daylight the darkest night."

There was no doubt in Will's mind after that first rehearsal that his company had the ability to do it. "They can make even a poor play seem good," he thought happily as he walked to his lodgings. "And I—I shall give them such plays as these boards have not yet seen. My apprentice days are over. I feel confident as I have never felt before."

11. *Problems with the Clown*

THERE was but one actor with whom Will foresaw any difficulty, and that was Kempe, the clown. For Will was determined that the kind of clowning Kempe was famous for should not intrude upon his plays.

Kempe was a law unto himself. He was so popular that he did whatever he liked on the stage. He would add lines to his part at will.

He would throw in jokes. He would mangle in ridiculous ways what had been set down for him to speak. He would suddenly start laughing and keep it up till the spectators had to laugh too. Or he would make funny faces and contort his body and do tricks to draw attention to himself while some important action of the play was going on. And he wore great flapping slippers that of themselves made people laugh.

Will could see that the players were annoyed by Kempe's antics. But no one tried to do anything about it. The audiences adored Will Kempe! The public loved his silly nonsense. Clowns were a tradition on the stage, and Londoners both expected and demanded clowning in every play, no matter how serious. Will knew that the writers had given up protesting long since and had bowed to the will of the people. Only Marlowe had never given in. He had refused to write any parts for clowns—but the only result of it was that someone else had written in the parts anyway.

" 'Tis impossible to cut the clowning out,"

thought Will. "Nor do I want to. Clowning is good, it has its place. But its place is *inside*, not *outside*, the play. 'Tis right the spectators should have their clown. But he must not be one who makes asides and plays tricks and laughs out of turn. The clown must be as solid a part of the play as any other character."

The question was whether Kempe could be made to see that that kind of clowning was better than his own. Unfortunately *Romeo and Juliet* had small occasion for clowning. Kempe's part was very brief. Would he consent to discipline himself and keep within the few lines given him?

Not only Will, but all the players were intensely interested in this question. At Will's insistence, they had it out in full with Kempe before they started rehearsing *Romeo and Juliet*. And it was a great relief to everybody that he proved to be not the stiff-necked fellow Will had feared he would be.

"Say no more," Kempe said. "It sticketh me sore, yet I will be ruled by you—curb my extemporal wit and speak no more than is set down for me. The groundlings will rage at it. But I'll do 't though they tear the stage down. Only let me have my jig at the end."

No one objected to that, it being the well-established custom for the players to dance together on the stage after every play. Will Kempe could do his famous leaping jig and welcome.

To everyone's surprise and satisfaction, the clown kept his word and held to the lines Will had given him. But from then on Will looked for opportunities to write suitable parts for Kempe.

A few months later he saw his chance. Every year at Christmas time the London players were called upon to present plays at Queen Elizabeth's court. For the Queen loved the stage and wanted to see the best the theaters produced. Partly because they were the best players in town, Will's company had the honor of presenting the first play at each Christmas season. But now a very special honor came to them. Lady Elizabeth Vere— Lord Burghley's granddaughter, whom the

Earl of Southampton had refused to wed—was going to be married to the young Earl of Derby. The wedding would be celebrated at the Queen's palace in Greenwich. And the Lord Chamberlain's Men were commanded to have a new play ready for part of the festivities.

"Will, we rely on you," James Burbage said. "Give us something light, amusing, pleasing, gay."

"Something out of mythology or the classics?" Will suggested. " 'Twould be fitting to the occasion."

"Set your imagination a-gallop and carry us where you will," said Burbage. "The Office of the Revels will provide the scenery and costumes as usual. And child actors will be available if you desire to use them."

"Children, you say . . ." said Will, and went home thinking.

Already an idea was taking hold of his mind. The children should be fairies! He would make a play of moonshine and madness—a midsummer night's dream. Puck, the fairy

The fairy queen would fall madly in love with a mortal

mischief-maker, should cause the fairy queen to fall madly in love with a mortal—the grossest, commonest, clumsiest, stupidest sort of mortal in the world—a very ass. And Puck should even contrive to give him a true ass's head.

"The court will love it," thought Will gleefully. "Who would not laugh to see the dainty queen dote on her love's long, hairy ears!"

But who should the stupid mortal be?

An actor! An Athenian weaver, turned actor. He would be one of a group of workmen who would come to the court of Athens to present a play at the wedding of their duke. The actors would hold a rehearsal in a wood— on the very spot where the fairy queen lay sleeping. There Puck would transform the weaver. At sight of the monster, the rest would flee and leave the stage set for the love scene of the fairy queen.

Will didn't hesitate a minute about the character he would give the weaver-actor. Ned Alleyn had sprung at once to his mind. Will had often seen how Ned behaved at rehearsals—always full of himself; always grabbing the best part; forever claiming he could do every and any part; full of suggestions as to how to get around this difficulty and that; telling everybody what to do.

How Will Kempe would clown the part! How he would strut and posture, over-act, be tragical, and tear his passion to tatters, ay to very rags!

12. *Strange, Hidden Places of the Human Heart*

KEMPE was not the only one pleased with his part in *A Midsummer Night's Dream*—the whole company was delighted with it. Under Will's teaching they had gradually overcome their faults, and they laughed now at the kind of exaggerated acting they had once thought the finest art. Besides, they were pleased enough to see Ned Alleyn ridiculed. For the Admiral's Men at the Rose were their rivals, and there was constant competition between the two companies. Although the whole town and the Thames lay between them, each group of players watched with keenest interest what went on in the other theater—what crowds they drew, what writers were working for them, what plays they put on, what London said of them.

At the moment Shakespeare's players felt very jubilant because *Romeo and Juliet* was immensely popular. Everybody was quoting the play. It had set the fashion in love-making among the gallants, who talked nothing but "pure Juliet and Romeo." The Lord Chamberlain's Men were proud of their Will Shakespeare. They knew they had the best playwright in London, and they felt confident that year after year he would keep on giving them plays that would be the talk of London. Let the Admiral's Men pay what they would, they could not hire such a writer as Will Shakespeare. There was none such to be hired. What they put on at the Rose was wretched stuff, mostly plays hastily slapped together by four or five third-rate hacks. If a good play was produced at the Rose, it was sure to be an old play revived. Their big drawing card was Ned Alleyn with his wonderful voice and his heroic way of acting.

Will was happy about the way everything was going at the Theater and gratified, too, that he had much more money in his pocket than ever before. He had always sent home what he could. Now he could send more. And he could live better. Instead of an attic room, he had taken a small house where he was more comfortable. But, strangely, he felt more alone there than in lodgings. A house, he found, was but an empty shell without a wife and children in it. Nearly all the players of his company had families—there was warmth and laughter and joy in their homes. When he visited John Heminges or Henry Condell, children fairly swarmed over him. And when he came back, his ears still ringing with their chatter, his silent house seemed like a reproach.

Will seldom wrote letters and even less often received them. Still he had always managed to get home once a year to pick up the strands of his broken life. After he had spent a day or two there, the longing to have his family in London would grow. Susanna had a very pretty wit. Hamnet was a boy in his own image. And Judith—Judith he loved all the more because she was a hoyden who climbed trees and would not ply her needle.

" 'Twould be good to have them around me," Will would say to himself. But then a troubled thought would break in on his longing. "How can I give my mind to the thousand small concerns of home and children when my days and nights are e'en now overfull? I have scarce time to sleep as 'tis. Anne can neither share my thoughts nor approve my work. She would be alone in London. And as for the children, 'tis better for them to romp in the fields, pluck cuckoo cups at will, and smell fresh air."

Some day, he thought, he would go back to Stratford and stay the remainder of his days. For the present he had to be in London. Its varied people, its excitement, its pageantry and, above all, its theaters and players were a necessity to him. "I could write plays nowhere else," he thought. But he had never accepted the city as his own. It was not London but Stratford-upon-Avon that he loved, and each time he went home he realized it more. London would never be home to him. His roots were in Warwickshire. And he smiled to think of the strange, hidden places of the human heart— that he should want to go back to the little town he had been so eager to leave!

There was a house in Stratford that Will had his eye on. As a boy this house had always stirred his imagination, partly because people said it had been built by a Lord Mayor of London and partly because it was the biggest and handsomest house in Stratford. Will had never been inside, but it was said to have ten fireplaces. To live in that house had once seemed to Will the height of any man's ambition. To own it seemed a distinction even now. As soon as he became a sharer, Will had begun to put money away to buy it.

"Why is that house important to me?" Will

once asked himself, looking deep into his heart
as he looked deep into the hearts of all. And he
answered, "I desire outward honor to match the
dignity I feel within."

Will knew well that it had been no small dis-
appointment to his father that his eldest son
should become an actor. "Nay, Will, nay. I'll
be no party to thy going," John Shakespeare

Will had his eye on the handsomest house in Stratford

had said when Will first disclosed his plans of
going to London. "To be a player is little better than to be a vagabond! I repent me that
ever I let thee go as chorister to Squire Houghton of Lea. I am a glover, Will, and a man of
substance. Thy mother was an Arden! True, I
was but a yeoman when I married her. But I
have built myself up, Will. I have been con-
stable and alderman and bailiff of this town
and will yet be a gentleman with coat of arms.
And shall I have a vagabond player for my
son?"

Many a time while he was still a hired man
Will had thought of his father's words. And
always the image of Stratford's many-chimneyed
house had risen in his mind. In London he
had seen actors who had built fortunes, bought
country estates, and become gentlemen. Some
day he, too, would take the stain of vagabondage from his name. He would come back to
Stratford a man of substance, move his family
into the finest house in town, and be a gentleman. His boy should yet be proud of having
been a player's son!

Early in August of 1596 Will Shakespeare suffered a painful setback to his dreams. He was on tour with his company when word reached him that Hamnet was very ill. Will hastened to Stratford. But he arrived only to find the boy already dead, and on the 11th of August he laid his son to rest.

13. *A Costly Mistake*

J AMES BURBAGE looked quietly around the table at the dozen sharers whom he had asked to meet at his house. "I have called you here, my friends," he said, "because I would fain have a little of your counsel if I could. You all know the trouble I am in. The Theater is mine, but not the land on which it stands. I little thought when I took a lease on't one-and-twenty years ago that I should not be able to renew it. But thus it is. 'Tis clear to me that I must build again—for the Curtain, as you well know, is but a makeshift not suited to our needs.

"Now the point, friends," Burbage continued, "is this: I am for building a theater of a quite different sort—and in this my sons Cuthbert and Richard are agreed with me. What I have in mind is a playhouse with a roof, a roof enclosing all—a playhouse lit by candlelight. In such a theater we could play in rain and snow, at night as in the daytime. In my mind's eye I see a theater that is select—no groundlings, seats for all, and prices high enough to attract only the better sort."

"Faith, you could not have it stand in Southwark then. There's naught select about that neighborhood," said Kempe.

"I have my eye on Blackfriars, Will," James Burbage said. "You know—that building of the old monastery where the Children of the Chapel acted. Blackfriars is in a choice part of the city."

"Ay, and outside the Corporation's control!" remarked Phillips, the company's chief musician.

"Thou hast it in a nutshell, Gus. The Corporation could not say 'no' to my building a theater there. . . . But wherefore dost thou shake thy head at me, Will Shakespeare?" James Burbage went on. "Come, let us have thy thoughts."

"I fear your audience 'of the better sort,' " said Will. "Nay, do not laugh—I am in earnest. 'Tis your groundlings that spur me to my best endeavor. 'Tis they keep my plays fast-moving; for ever I must hold in mind that the apprentices must stand. I am well suited with the audience we have. I care not to make plays to please the learned."

"Thou shalt write as thou wilt. Thy playmaking's not in question."

Will kept his peace after that. He was but a sharer. James Burbage was the theater owner, responsible for the rent and upkeep of the playhouse, and receiving half the takings of the galleries as his share. "Though he asks for counsel," thought Will, "he will make the decision himself—and live to regret it."

But it was with the approval of everyone save Will that James Burbage bought the Blackfriars property. All were carried away by the manager's idea. Burbage had thrown his whole heart into the project, and they watched with enthusiasm while his dream took rapid shape. Then, when the theater was nearly finished, suddenly all realized that their manager had made a terrible mistake. The neighborhood he had chosen was *too* exclusive. Though the Corporation could not object to a theater, the residents could.

What! A public theater in their select midst? Riff-raff coming and going? They would not put up with the noise! They would not endure the nuisance!

The residents got up a petition with a lot of important signatures at the end, laid it before the Privy Council, and got what they wanted. James Burbage must cease and desist from making a theater in that neighborhood.

" 'Tis a heavy blow, lads, a heavy blow," the

old manager told his sons. "I'm seven-and-sixty, nigh man's allotted span of three-score-and-ten. Yet I never bowed my head till now."

He had invested a huge sum in the venture. The loss was more than he could bear—and in less than two months James Burbage was dead.

14. *The Theater Comes Down*

CUTHBERT BURBAGE, Richard's elder brother, was not a player and had never taken part in the actors' affairs before. But now he took it upon himself to get a theater for them. Refusing 'no' for an answer, he went again to Giles Alleyn, the owner of the land on which the Theater stood. Cuthbert offered him this inducement and that. For a year and a half he worked to bring the man around. And just when he thought he had the matter clinched, Giles Alleyn backed out.

Cuthbert was furious. "All wasted, all wasted, all for naught!" he fumed. "And now the rogue talks of pulling the Theater down and using the wood for some 'better' purpose. Richard, we cannot allow it! Something must be done."

"And shall be!" old Mrs. Burbage declared, striking the table with her strong, wrinkled hand. "Your father, lads, built the Theater with his own hands. Every penny he had or could borrow went into it. And Giles Alleyn shall not have a stick of it."

"Cuthbert," said Richard, "doth not our old lease say 'tis we who have the right to take down the Theater and carry away the wood?"

"We *had* the right before the lease was up. But the one-and-twenty years are run out."

"And what o' that?" Mrs. Burbage snapped. "Ye are not your father's sons an ye let that hinder ye. Is there not land enow to be leased beyond the Thames? Take down the Theater and set it up in Southwark! An ye let that

Giles Alleyn lay his filthy hand to the Theater——"

"Hush, Mother, pray! We have not the money to rebuild the Theater even if we did take it down."

"Then ask the sharers for it. I'll warrant some o' them have money."

As a result of the old lady's prodding, Cuthbert and Richard hastily called five of the sharers into their councils. The men the brothers chose were Will Shakespeare, Augustine Phillips, John Heminges, Thomas Pope, and Will Kempe.

"Richard and I," said Cuthbert when the case had been set before them, "will put up half the money toward building a theater in a new neighborhood if you five between you will put up the other half."

"Each of us would then own one-tenth," Phillips considered.

"Aye," said Cuthbert. "As 'housekeepers' each of you would receive one-tenth of the first takings besides your due as sharers."

"I will go in with you," Will Shakespeare said.

"And I," each of the others agreed.

"Then, friends, 'tis as good as done," said Richard. "Cuthbert here has found the best possible site across the river. Close to the Rose, but nearer London Bridge, so that people walking across must pass us first!"

"Look you now," said Cuthbert, "Giles Alleyn is out of town. We must act quickly—before he returns."

On Christmas Day, Cuthbert and Richard Burbage with the five other "housekeepers" took over the plot for the new theater. Three days later the Burbages brought master-carpenter Peter Smith and a dozen of his workmen to the Theater. And while old Mrs. Burbage stood by, enjoying the proceedings, they started pulling the building down.

"What dost thou there, man?"

Richard looked by his elbow and saw a little man with a red, angry face, who was waving his arms about in such a ridiculous fashion that Richard could not keep from laughing.

"Ye'll laugh t'other side o' your mouth 'fore Giles Alleyn is done with ye!" the little man screamed.

"And what might your interest in the matter be?" asked Cuthbert, coming up.

"Interest, is it? I'm set to look after Alleyn's

The Theater's lumber was transported to the new site

property in his absence," the man answered. "And I ask ye what's the meaning o' this?"

"We're taking the building down for repairs," said Richard coolly. "Look up there! See'st thou not how rotten that beam is? 'Tis a hazard to life and limb."

"Faith, ye'll not blind me. 'Tis the first time ever I heard of a house taken down for repairs," the little man said. "In the name of Giles Alleyn I order ye to stop!"

"And in the name of thy own good health I tell thee to save thy breath to cool thy porridge," Richard said and turned his back.

In a few days the Theater was down. The lumber was ferried across the Thames to the new site. And while Alleyn shouted and threatened and went fruitlessly to law, the new playhouse—a little larger, a little more convenient than the Theater, but built on the same plan—rose on its foundations. The "housekeepers" named it the *Globe*. And for an emblem they took Hercules carrying the world on his shoulders.

15. *In the Making*

WILL SHAKESPEARE stood in the pit of the darkening Globe and gazed about him at the octagonal walls. A few more weeks would see the theater completed. The three galleries were still without a rail. The thatched roofing that would protect the topmost was not yet in place. But the pit was already paved, and the stage, rising four feet from the ground and jutting out to the middle of the theater, was done. Only the low railing that would run round its edge was missing.

What pageantry would march across those boards? What kings and queens, nobles, merchants and ladies, citizens, soldiers, peasants, clowns would pass in and out those doors? The whole living world was his to call upon. Fancy was his. All history was his. Captains and kings—whosoever he summoned must at his bidding step from the shadows, walk, think, speak, feel, and live again his little hour upon the stage.

"Ah, Will, a noble theater!" Richard Burbage's voice broke in on Will's thoughts. Clambering on the stage, Richard walked with measured step to the rear. " 'Tis as we planned it," he said. "Nine-and-twenty feet. Double that maketh it eight-and-fifty from wall to wall." His eyes swept the galleries, took in the pit. " 'Twill hold, I judge, a quarter again as many as the Theater—about two thousand. How sounds my voice, Will?

" 'Once more unto the breach, dear friends
        once more;
Or close the wall up with our English dead!' "

"Excellent, excellent! Ah, Richard, thou mak'st my Henry live indeed," said Will. "And 'twill sound far better when the theater is full."

"Peter Smith hath promised Cuthbert the last nail shall be in by middle August," Richard said when he had leaped down from the stage. "We'll open with your play, Will, charge double the first day, and if the play takes—as I doubt not it will—we'll run it a full week. What have you writ for us, Will? A comedy?"

"Nay, a tragedy—*Julius Caesar*. . . . What, shall we forth?"

With a "good night" to the watchman, they left the Globe and walked toward the river.

"*Julius Caesar*, you say?"

"Ay, the murder of Caesar at the Capitol and all that followed after. I have it well along—I could read it to the company e'en now."

The boatmen's cries, "Westward ho!" had been audible to them almost as soon as they

left the theater. Now at the river shore the
traffic took all their attention. They hailed a
boat and crossed to the other bank. Already it
was night, and in the houses candles gleamed
like glow-worms.

Will had always held to the custom of intro-
ducing a play to the company before the parts
were distributed among the actors. He would
outline the plot, give a notion of the characters, and read aloud some of the important
passages. But no matter how many times he
did it, he always approached the reading with
a beating heart. The players were his first
audience. When he faced his fellow actors
around a table, the sureness he felt in his own
room always fled. How would his work go
over? He could judge by the players' stillness
even more than by what they said afterwards.
The test was in the silence. When not a hand
stirred, nor foot shifted, nor eye left his face
as he read, he knew he had a good play.

This time he felt less sure than ever; for he
had never written a play of character before.

He had taken the story of *Julius Caesar* out
of a book he had picked up by chance on a
stall—*Plutarch's Lives*. When he pored over it,
Will had felt curiously close to Plutarch.
"That old Roman was my fellow," he thought.
"He was interested less in what men do than
in what they are and why they do it." To Will
the characters and tangled lives of Caesar,
Brutus, and Mark Antony as Plutarch pictured
them seemed the very stuff of drama ready to
his hand. He had taken what he wanted—and
out of it had rebuilt an unforgettable moment
in history.

Had he made it live? Would the players,
now laughing and jesting as they sat around
the table in Richard's house, lose themselves
in the story? Would they give their emotions
into his keeping—to the very end?

16. *Will Reads His Play*

"COME, 'tis strucken nine," said Richard. "Wife, sit thee down here by me. . . . Now, Will, let's hear your play."

"Friends, you may perchance wonder," Will began, "that I have called my play *Julius Caesar*. For he is murdered early in the action. But you will see—his spirit ranges through the play and takes revenge on them that spilled his blood.

"Now, here's the setting:

"When we open, Caesar is supreme in Rome. There is a senate, of course, but Caesar makes naught of it. He has taken to using a sceptre and a throne, and is well on the way to being king. Some few are alarmed at his ambition. More are envious—and of these Cassius is the moving spirit.

"He and Caesar were boys together and now it galls Cassius that Caesar is become a god while he must bend his body if Caesar so much as carelessly nod on him. Lean, sour, unsmiling, Cassius has made up his mind to do away with Caesar. And already he has won some noble Romans to his cause. For Cassius is a keen observer. He knows each man's particular weakness and knows how to play upon it. This man he has won through envy, that one through ambition, a third because of injury at Caesar's hands. Most of all Cassius would have his brother-in-law Brutus join the conspirators. But he knows well that Brutus may not be won through any weakness. For Brutus is the noblest Roman of them all.

"This Brutus must be very carefully played,

friends. He is a hero such as I have never wrought before. Brutus is destroyed not by the evil in him—for there is not one jot of it in him—but by the good. He is *too* noble, *too* trusting, *too* generous, *too* unworldly. He loves Caesar above all other men and joins the conspirators only because he holds the general good above his own. Rome is more to him than Caesar. 'Not that I loved Caesar less,' he says, 'but that I loved Rome more.'

"It is thus through his strength—rather than any weakness in him—that Cassius seeks to win Brutus over. And the occasion of it is this:

"On the holiday with which the play opens, Caesar's good friend Mark Antony offers him a crown. Now, Caesar has been yearning for a crown and would fain have taken it. But to impress the multitude, he makes a show of refusing. At this the people clap their hands and shout with joy. Whereupon Caesar dares not accept the crown, though Antony offers it him a second and a third time.

"Cassius and Brutus have meanwhile stood speaking together within hearing of the noise.

" 'What means this shouting?' Brutus asks. 'I do fear the people choose Caesar for their king.'

" 'Ay, do you fear it?' Cassius says, seizing upon the words. 'Then must I think you would not have it so.'

" 'I would not, Cassius; yet I love him well.'

"Thereupon Cassius begins to play on Brutus. 'I cannot tell what you and other men think of this life,' he says; 'but, for my single self, I would as lief not live as live to be in awe of such a thing as I myself. I was born free as Caesar; so were you. We both have fed as well, and we can both endure the winter's cold as well as he. . . . Brutus and Caesar: what should be in that *Caesar?* Write them together, yours is as fair a name; sound them, it doth become the mouth as well; weigh them, it is as heavy; conjure with 'em, Brutus will start a spirit as soon as Caesar. Now, in the names of all the gods at once, upon what meat doth this our Caesar feed that he is grown so great? Age, thou art shamed! Rome, thou hast lost the breed of noble bloods! When went there by an age but it was famed with

more than with *one* man? When could they
say till now, that talked of Rome, that her
wide walls encompassed but *one* man?'

"Well, Brutus is by degrees won over. But
he joins with a heavy heart. And he would
have as little bloodshed as possible. When
Cassius insists they should also kill Mark
Antony because he may prove troublesome,
Brutus holds against it.

" 'Our course will seem too bloody, Caius

Will was reading from his new play Julius Caesar

Cassius,' he says, 'to cut the head off and then hack the limbs. For Antony is but a limb of Caesar. Let us be sacrificers, but not butchers, Caius. We all stand up against the spirit of Caesar; and in the spirit of men there is no blood. O, that we then could come by Caesar's spirit and not dismember Caesar! But, alas, Caesar must bleed for it! And, gentle friends, let's kill him boldly, but not wrathfully. Let's carve him as a dish fit for the gods, not hew him as a carcass fit for hounds. And as for Mark Antony, think not of him; for he can do no more than Caesar's arm when Caesar's head is off.'

"Now, the conspirators have planned to kill Caesar in the Capitol on the ides of March, which is the fifteenth of the month. But they fear that Caesar may keep at home that day; for a soothsayer hath warned him to beware the ides of March, and Caesar is grown superstitious of late. So they decide that some of themselves shall go to escort Caesar to the Capitol. And it is well they do. For Caesar hath yielded to his wife's pleading and promised Calpurnia he will stay at home. At this moment the first of the conspirators arrives.

" 'Caesar, all hail! I come to fetch you to the senate-house.'

" 'And you are come in very happy time,' says Caesar, 'to bear my greeting to the senators and tell them that I will not come today. *Cannot* is false, and that I *dare* not, falser. I *will* not come to-day. Tell them so, Decius.'

" 'Say he is sick,' Calpurnia puts in.

" 'Shall Caesar send a lie? Have I in conquest stretched mine arm so far, to be afeard to tell graybeards the truth? Decius, go tell them Caesar *will* not come.'

" 'Most mighty Caesar, let me know some cause, lest I be laughed at when I tell them so.'

" 'The cause,' says Caesar, 'is in my will: I *will* not come. That is enough to satisfy the senate. But for your private satisfaction, because I love you, I will let you know: Calpurnia here, my wife, stays me at home.' And he tells Decius about a dream she had wherein Caesar's statue ran blood and many smiling Romans came and bathed their hands in it.

" 'This dream,' Decius protests, 'is all amiss interpreted. It was a vision fair and fortunate. Your statue spouting blood in many pipes, in which so many smiling Romans bathed, signifies that from you great Rome shall suck reviving blood.' Besides, he says, Caesar must come because the senate has decided to give him a crown this day. 'If you shall send them word you will not come, their minds may change. And it were a mock for some one to say, *Break up the senate till another time when Caesar's wife shall meet with better dreams.* If Caesar hide himself, shall they not whisper, *Lo, Caesar is afraid?*'

"Caesar is convinced, and just as he is, the other conspirators arrive. Mark Antony comes immediately after. And they all go off to the Capitol together. . . .''

Will paused and stole a glance around the table, where all sat motionless.

" 'Tis strong, Will,'' Richard said at last. "Brutus, Cassius, Caesar—you have fine contrasts there—all wonderful parts to play.''

"Wait till you hear Mark Antony,'' said Will.

17. *Murder in the Capitol*

"GO TO, bring on the murder, Will," John Heminges said. "Thou hast us here suspended in mid air."

"Ay, the murder! Let's have the murder!" the rest clamored.

"Now the killing," Will continued, "has been planned thus: Trebonius shall draw Mark Antony away. Then Metellus Cimber shall approach Caesar and plead that his banished brother be permitted to return. Brutus

and Cassius shall add their pleas—and Casca
shall be the first to strike.

"As they fully expect, Caesar refuses. 'I could
be well moved,' he says, 'if I were as you. If
I could pray to move, prayers would move me.
But I am constant as the northern star. The
skies are painted with unnumbered sparks.
They are all fire and every one doth shine.
But there's but one in all doth hold his place.
So in the world. 'Tis furnished well with men,
yet in the number I do know but one that is
unshaked of motion. And that I am he, let me
a little show it even in this: that I was constant
Cimber should be banished, and constant do
remain to keep him so.'

" 'Speak, hands, for me!' Casca cries and
plunges his dagger in. After him all the other
conspirators stab Caesar, and Brutus slowly
last of all.

" '*Et tu*, Brute!' the dying Caesar murmurs.
'Then fall, Caesar!'

" 'Liberty! Freedom! Tyranny is dead! Run
hence, proclaim, cry it about the streets!'

" 'People and senators,' Brutus shouts, 'be

" 'Et tu, Brute!' *the dying Caesar murmurs.*"

not affrighted! Fly not; stand still; ambition's
debt is paid.' Then turning to the conspirators,
he says, 'Stoop, Romans, and let us bathe our
hands in Caesar's blood up to the elbows, and
besmear our swords. Then walk we forth, even
to the market place, and, waving our red
weapons o'er our heads, let's all cry, *Peace,
freedom, and liberty*!'

"Now Mark Antony has fled to his house amazed, but presently his servant comes running up and kneels before Brutus. If Brutus will vouch that Antony may safely come to him, he says, and know why Caesar hath deserved to die, Mark Antony will not love Caesar dead so much as Brutus living.

" 'Thy master is a wise and valiant Roman; I never thought him worse,' says Brutus. 'Tell him, so please him come unto this place, he shall be satisfied; and, by my honor, depart untouched.'

"So Antony comes. 'O mighty Caesar!' he says, beholding Caesar's body. 'Dost thou lie so low? Are all thy conquests, glories, triumphs, spoils, shrunk to this little measure? Fare thee well. . . . I know not, gentlemen, what you intend, who else must be let blood, who else is rank. If I myself, there is no hour so fit as Caesar's death hour, nor no instrument of half that worth as those your swords, made rich with the most noble blood of all this world. I do beseech ye, if you bear me hard, now, whilst your purple hands do reek and smoke, fulfil your pleasure. Live a thousand years, I shall not find myself so apt to die. No place will please me so, no mean of death, as here by Caesar, and by you cut off, the choice and master spirits of this age.'

" 'O Antony,' Brutus says, 'beg not your death of us. Though now we must appear bloody and cruel, yet see you but our hands and this the bleeding business they have done. Our hearts you see not. They are pitiful, and pity to the general wrong of Rome hath done this deed on Caesar. For your part, to you our swords have leaden points, and our hearts do receive you in with all kind love, good thoughts, and reverence.'

" 'Your voice,' says Cassius, 'shall be as strong as any man's in the disposing of new dignities.'

" 'Only be patient,' Brutus says, 'till we have appeased the multitude, beside themselves with fear, and then we will deliver you the cause, why I, that did love Caesar when I struck him, have thus proceeded.'

"Then Antony shakes each of the conspira-

tors by the hand. 'Friends am I with you all
and love you all, upon this hope, that you shall
give me reasons why and wherein Caesar was
dangerous.'

" 'Our reasons are so full of good regard,'
says Brutus, 'that were you, Antony, the son
of Caesar, you should be satisfied.'

" 'That's all I seek,' Antony replies. And
then he asks if he may bring Caesar's body to
the market place and in the pulpit, as becomes
a friend, speak in the order of his funeral.

" 'You shall, Mark Antony,' Brutus grants.

"But Cassius here quickly draws Brutus
aside. 'You know not what you do! Do not
consent that Antony speak in his funeral!
Know you how much the people may be moved
by that which he will utter?'

" 'By your pardon,' Brutus replies, 'I will
myself into the pulpit first and show the reason of our Caesar's death. . . . Mark Antony,
here, take you Caesar's body. You shall not in
your funeral speech blame us, but speak all
good you can devise of Caesar, and say you
do't by our permission. Else shall you not have

any hand at all about his funeral. And you shall speak in the same pulpit whereto I am going, after my speech is ended.'

" 'Be it so; I do desire no more.'

"With this they go out, leaving Antony alone with Caesar's body. And as soon as they are gone, Mark Antony throws off his mask.

" 'O pardon me, thou bleeding piece of earth,' he says, 'that I am meek and gentle with these butchers! Thou art the ruins of the noblest man that ever lived in the tide of times. Woe to the hand that shed this costly blood!' "

18. *The Fickle Mob*

"NOW CAESAR had been the people's idol," Will continued. "So coming to the public square, Cassius and Brutus find an angry, threatening multitude. 'We will be satisfied!' the people cry; 'let us be satisfied!' Some follow Cassius, others remain to hear Brutus. And he, mounting into the pulpit, quickly convinces them that Caesar was killed for freedom's sake.

" 'Had you rather Caesar were living,'
Brutus ends, 'and die all slaves, than that
Caesar were dead, to live all free men? As
Caesar loved me, I rejoice at it; as he was
valiant, I honor him; but as he was ambitious,
I slew him. . . . Who is here so base that would
be a bondman? If any, speak; for him have I
offended. Who is here so rude that would not
be a Roman? If any, speak, for him have I
offended. Who is here so vile that will not love
his country? If any, speak, for him have I
offended.'

" 'None, Brutus, none!'

"He has won the people over. All are now
convinced that Caesar was a tyrant whom they
are well rid of. The fickle populace would
carry Brutus home in triumph to his house,
but he entreats that not a man depart save him
alone till they have heard Antony speak.

"He comes now, bearing Caesar's body, and
at once sees what has happened. He means, of
course, to undo Brutus's work and so to play
on the citizens' emotions that they shall rise
and mutiny. But he knows he must move

craftily—in their present temper 'tis dangerous
to speak either good of Caesar or ill of the
conspirators.

"He mounts into the pulpit.

" 'Friends!' he calls out above the hubbub.
Then louder, 'Romans!' Still the din goes on.
'Countrymen, lend me your ears! . . . I come
to bury Caesar, not to praise him. The evil
that men do lives after them; the good is oft
interred with their bones. So let it be with
Caesar. The noble Brutus hath told you Caesar
was ambitious. If it were so, it was a grievous
fault, and grievously hath Caesar answered
it. . . . Here, under leave of Brutus and the
rest—for Brutus is an honorable man; so are
they all, all honorable men—come I to speak
in Caesar's funeral. He was my friend, faithful
and just to me. But Brutus says he was ambitious; and Brutus is an honorable man.'

"Antony has pacified the crowd and now
thinks he may proceed to sow the seeds of
doubt.

" 'He has brought many captives home to
Rome, whose ransoms did the general coffers

"Friends, Romans, countrymen, lend me your ears!"

fill. Did this in Caesar seem ambitious? When that the poor have cried, Caesar hath wept; ambition should be made of sterner stuff. Yet Brutus says he was ambitious; and Brutus is an honorable man. You all did see that on the Lupercal I thrice presented him a kingly crown, which he did thrice refuse. Was this ambition? Yet Brutus says he was ambitious; and, sure, he is an honorable man. I speak not to disprove what Brutus spoke, but here I am to speak what I do know. . . .

" 'You all did love him once, not without cause. What cause withholds you, then, to mourn for him? O judgment, thou art fled to brutish beasts, and men have lost their reason!'

"Here Antony breaks down, and tears—called forth by grief, anger, excitement, but most of all with intent to move the multitude—pour from his eyes. 'Bear with me,' he says, turning to wipe the drops away; 'my heart is in the coffin there with Caesar, and I must pause till it come back to me.'

"All are moved. 'If thou consider of the

matter rightly, Caesar has had great wrong,' says one.

" 'Has he, masters? I fear there will a worse come in his place.'

" 'Marked ye his words? He would not take the crown; therefore 'tis certain he was not ambitious.'

" 'If it be found so, some will dearly pay for it.'

" 'Poor soul! His eyes are red as fire with weeping.'

"Now Antony speaks again. 'But yesterday the word of Caesar might have stood against the world; now lies he there, and none so poor to do him reverence. O masters, if I were disposed to stir your hearts and minds to mutiny and rage, I should do Brutus wrong, and Cassius wrong, who, you all know, are honorable men. I will not do them wrong; I rather choose to wrong the dead, to wrong myself and you, than I will wrong such honorable men.'

"Taking a scroll from his bosom, Antony holds it aloft. 'But here's a parchment with

the seal of Caesar. I found it in his closet. 'Tis
his will. Let but the commons hear this testa-
ment—which, pardon me, I do not mean to
read—and they would go and kiss dead Caesar's
wounds, and dip their napkins in his sacred
blood, yea, beg a hair of him for memory, and,
dying, mention it in their wills, bequeathing
it as a rich legacy unto their issue.'

" 'We'll hear the will! Read it, Mark
Antony!'

" 'Have patience, gentle friends, I must *not*
read it; it is not fitting you should know how
Caesar loved you. You are not wood, you are
not stones, but men; and, being men, hearing
the will of Caesar, it will inflame you, it will
make you mad. 'Tis good you know not that
you are his heirs; for if you should, O, what
would come of it!'

" 'Read the will! We'll hear it, Antony.
You *shall* read us the will, Caesar's will.'

" 'Will you be patient?' Antony asks. 'Will
you stay awhile? I have gone too far to tell you
of it. I fear I wrong the honorable men whose
daggers have stabbed Caesar; I do fear it.'

" 'They were traitors!' a citizen cries. 'Honorable men!'

" 'They were villains, murderers! The will! Read the will!'

" 'You will *compel* me, then, to read the will? . . . Then make a ring about the corpse of Caesar, and let me show you him that made the will. Shall I descend? And will you give me leave?'

" 'Come down!' the people cry. And Antony descends.

" 'If you have tears, prepare to shed them now. . . . You all do know this mantle. I remember the first time ever Caesar put it on; 'twas on a summer's evening, in his tent, that day he overcame the Nervii. Look, in this place ran Cassius' dagger through. See what a rent the envious Casca made! Through this the well-beloved Brutus stabbed, and as he plucked his cursed steel away, mark how the blood of Caesar followed it, as rushing out of doors, to make sure if Brutus so unkindly knocked, or no; for Brutus, as you know, was Caesar's angel. Judge, O you gods, how dearly Caesar

loved him! This was the most unkindest cut
of all; for when the noble Caesar saw him stab,
ingratitude, more strong than traitors' arms,
quite vanquished him. Then burst his mighty
heart; and, in his mantle muffling up his face,
even at the base of Pompey's statue—which all
the while ran blood—great Caesar fell. O what
a fall was there, my countrymen! Then I, and
you, and all of us fell down, while bloody trea-
son triumphed over us. . . . O, now you weep;
and I perceive you feel the force of pity. These
are gracious drops. Kind souls, what, weep you
when you but behold our Caesar's *vesture*
wounded?' He strips the mantle off. 'Look you
here, here is *himself*, marred, as you see, with
traitors!'

" 'We will be revenged!' the people cry.
'About! Seek! Burn! Fire! Kill! Slay! Let not
a traitor live!'

" 'Good friends, sweet friends!' Antony cries.
'Let me not stir you up to such a sudden flood
of mutiny. They that have done this deed are
wise and honorable, and will, no doubt, with
reason answer you. I come not, friends, to steal

away your hearts. I am no orator, as Brutus is; but, as you know me all, a plain blunt man that love my friend. And that they know full well that gave me public leave to speak of him. For I have neither wit, nor words, nor worth, action, nor utterance, nor the power of speech to stir men's blood. I only speak right on. I tell you that which you yourselves do know; show you sweet Caesar's wounds—poor, poor dumb mouths—and bid them speak for me. But were I Brutus, and Brutus Antony, there were an Antony would ruffle up your spirits, and put a tongue in every wound of Caesar, that should move the *stones* of Rome to rise and mutiny.'

" 'We'll mutiny!' the people cry.

" 'We'll burn the house of Brutus!'

" 'Away, then! Come, seek the conspirators!'

" 'Why, friends,' Antony says, 'you go to do you know not what. Wherein hath Caesar thus deserved your loves? Alas, you know not—I must tell you, then. You have forgot the will I told you of. Here is the will, and under Caesar's seal. To every Roman citizen he

gives, to every separate man, seventy-five
drachmas!'

" 'Most noble Caesar!'

" 'Moreover,' Antony continues, 'he hath
left you all his walks, his private arbors and
new-planted orchards, on this side Tiber. He
hath left them you and to your heirs for ever,
common pleasures, to walk abroad and recre-
ate yourselves. Here was a Caesar! When comes
such another?'

" 'Never, never!' the people cry. And bearing Caesar's body in their midst, they go off
to fire the houses of the conspirators.

" 'Now let it work,' Antony says. 'Mischief,
thou art afoot; take thou what course thou
wilt!' "

19. *The Noblest Roman of Them All*

WILL looked up from his manuscript, but no one spoke.

"How like you it?" he asked at last.

"Thou hast me so choked up," John Heminges said, "I cannot speak."

" 'Tis stirring, without question," said Henry Condell. "If none would bear me hard, I would bespeak the part of Antony. I have it so clear in my mind how thou mean'st to have the villain played, Will."

"O never a villain, Harry! Play him not as villain! Antony is a large figure, hot-blooded, generous, a man who can love right well. 'Tis true he seeks to make his power secure. But he is honest in avenging Caesar, whom he did truly love."

"Master Shakespeare, are there no women but Calpurnia in the play?" Richard's apprentice asked.

"There's Brutus's wife—Portia. That's the role for you, lad. A very noble lady. Being distraught at Brutus's absence and Mark Antony's growing power, she swallows fire and dies."

"I would fain hear what happens after," Winifred Burbage said.

"Why, after the funeral oration, Mistress Burbage, civil strife breaks out. Brutus and Cassius raise a force and go to meet Antony. Shall I briefly run o'er the rest?"

"Ay, Will, let's have it," Richard said, speaking for all.

"Well, on the eve of the battle Brutus, encamped on the plains of Philippi, cannot sleep for grieving over the news of Portia's death. He sits late reading in his tent, when of a sudden Caesar's ghost appears to him.

" 'Art thou some god, some angel, or some devil,' Brutus asks, 'that makest my blood cold and my hair to stare? Speak to me what thou art.'

" 'Thy evil spirit, Brutus.'

" 'Why comest thou?'

" 'To tell thee that thou shalt see me at Philippi.'

" 'Well,' says Brutus, 'then I shall see thee again?'

" 'Ay, at Philippi,' the ghost replies and vanishes.

"Now, Brutus and Cassius have staked everything on this one battle, but neither believes they will come out of it alive. So before they go forth into the fight, they embrace for the last time.

" 'For ever and for ever, farewell, Cassius!' Brutus says. 'If we do meet again, why, we shall smile; if not, why then this parting were well made.'

" 'For ever and for ever, farewell, Brutus! If we do meet again, we'll smile indeed; if not, 'tis true this parting was well made.'

The battle was fought on the plains of Philippi

"So the battle is fought, and ever Caesar's spirit hovers o'er it to take revenge. Cassius is first to fall. He is directing his troops from a hill when his bondman, Pindarus, comes running to tell him he must fly farther off because Mark Antony is already setting fire to his tents. But Cassius will not move. Instead, he bids his friend Titinius ride to find out if the troops he sees approaching be friend or enemy. His sight being ever thick, Cassius tells Pindarus to climb higher and report what happens. And Pindarus mistakes what he doth see. They are victorious troops, sent by Brutus. But Pindarus reports that Titinius is surrounded and taken.

" 'O coward that I am,' Cassius cries, 'to live so long to see my best friend taken before my face!' And he commands Pindarus to slay him.

"That starts the chain. Titinius, finding his friend dead, kills himself with Cassius' sword. Whereupon Brutus comes on and finds them both dead. 'O Julius Caesar,' he says, 'thou art mighty yet! Thy spirit walks abroad, and turns our swords in our own proper entrails. . . . Friends, I owe more tears to this dead man than you shall see me pay. I shall find time, Cassius, I shall find time.' And he goes out to fight the last fight. It is the end; for Antony has the victory and Brutus refuses to be taken captive. Bidding his servant Strato hold his sword, Brutus runs upon it. 'Caesar, now be still,' he says, dying. 'I killed not thee with half so good a will.'

"And now comes the final scene. Antony

with his friends comes on to take Brutus pris-
oner, but finds only his body. He is deeply
moved, and his generous words almost, but
not quite, close the play:

" 'This was the noblest Roman of them all.
All the conspirators save only he did that they
did in envy of great Caesar; he only, in a general honest thought and common good to all,
made one of them. His life was gentle, and
the elements so mixed in him that Nature
might stand up and say to all the world, *This
was a man!*' "

Will put the manuscript down. "There's
plenty of blood in it," said Will Sly after a
pause. "Caesar, Titinius, Cassius, Brutus—I
make it four bladders of sheep's blood we'll
need."

"That running on the sword will be ticklish
business, Will," Gus Phillips said. "Whoever
plays Brutus had better take care to practice
betimes."

"Richard," Will said, "you are the man for
Brutus. You were in my mind's eye when I

wrote the part—I heard you speak the lines."

"And what part dost thou desire, Will?" Henry Condell asked.

"I care not what part I play, so be it ye all are content."

Richard broke into a merry laugh. "Friends," he said, "I've brought poor Henslowe to mind. Our Globe will open with such a triumph that 'twill shake down the Rose. Henslowe will go mad at it. Since Ned Alleyn retired, the Rose has had no drawing card at all."

"Ay, there's but one Richard Burbage in London," Will said.

"And one Will Shakespeare in the world!" John Heminges added.

20. *At the Mermaid*

WILL SHAKESPEARE laid down his knife, pushed his plate aside, and leaned back against the Mermaid's partitioned wall.

"What, are ye done so soon?" John Heminges exclaimed. "Thou dost insult the Mermaid's specialty."

"Leave us not to finish the pasty alone!" Henry Condell protested.

"Here cometh one that will ease your trial—

a trencherman if e'er I saw one." Will nodded toward the entrance as he said this, and his companions, looking to the door, beheld a short, stocky figure advancing toward their stall.

Condell's face fell. "Prithee, ask not Ben Jonson to join us!" he whispered in alarm. "I cannot abide the man. He will haul out his unities and din them in our ears. I've had enough and too much of his learning already."

"He will not pause for invitation," Will returned.

"Ah, Shakespeare!" the newcomer said, seating himself without ceremony by Will. "I had not hoped to find you here. Heminges and Condell, too. And . . . what have we here? A fish pasty if my nose deceive me not." He brought his large, pockmarked face close to the dish and took so hungry a sniff that Heminges was forced to beckon the waiter for another plate.

"Gentlemen," Ben Jonson began, dipping crust into gravy with satisfaction, "deal plainly, do not flatter me. How like you my *Every Man Out of His Humour?*"

"Better than I like your manners in the gallery," said Condell with heat. " 'Tis enough to make a man forget his lines to see you making faces like one in pain if the rendering doth not please you!"

"Tush, tush, man. If thou stab me, I must wince. 'Tis the best to come from my pen, and I like ill to see it misplayed. How shall ye learn but by correction?"

"Correction call you it? A new name for ill manners! Will here has been pained times out of mind, but he hath the breeding to hide it."

"Have done, Harry," Will chid gently. "Your play," he said to Jonson, "is not the sort of comedy that calls for belly laughter, but I sensed the spectators were pleased."

"Belly laughter! Is't the function of comedy to set the pit aroaring? Nay, to win the mind from wickedness to virtue. Plautus and Terence have taught——"

"A plague on the Romans!" Heminges broke

Ben Jonson

out. "We came not to the Mermaid to hear the prate of them."

"He'll serve you up the unities now," Condell groaned.

"The unities, ay, the unities which Will Shakespeare, craving his pardon, doth woefully neglect."

"I see not why I should hold to them," Will said. "Wherefore must I have all my action *united*? Why must all hap on the same day, at the same time, in the same place? 'Tis too con-

fining. How can a character develop without
time and changing circumstance?"

"Will Shakespeare," Jonson said, helping
himself generously to more of the pasty, "let
me teach thee the classic principles of comedy.
A comedy character hath no need to develop.
It *is*. This man is a braggart, that one a glutton,
the third a pedant——"

"And if he be all three?" Condell asked
pointedly. But his shaft missed its mark.

"A comedy character is a stage character and
never all three. Each must represent a single
quality, which the audience will recognize at
once."

"But, Ben, I think you hold that we must
mirror life. I take my characters as I find them,"
Will said.

"And some that you find not at all," Jonson
retorted. "Fairies, forsooth! You trifle, you
trifle with the stage, Will Shakespeare. All your
care is for delight. And teaching goeth by the
board; so all is lost. What hath your *Julius
Caesar* to say? I grant you it hath pleased the
fat judgment of the multitude, but I hold there

are things ridiculous in it. And as for your comedies, they are insufferable—trifles, trifles all. Call you that a worthy plot—a duke to be in love with a countess, and that countess to be in love with the duke's son, and the son to be in love with the lady's waiting-woman? Or some such cross-wooing as that. Give them a clown to a serving-man and you have the dish seasoned. Where's the value in't? The stage hath a higher purpose than to amuse. And that purpose," he added, emphasizing each word with a bang of his knife on the table, "is to mirror the times and expose the deformity of the age."

He looked again into the pasty, but save for some spoonfuls of gravy the dish was empty, and he pushed back his plate.

" 'Tis clear," said Will, "we are worlds apart."

"Ay, 'tis clear we are," Jonson said. "But I trust I will yet bring the stage back to the glorious light of Rome. Ere I die I shall see 't again a copy of life, a mirror of custom, a show of truth."

With never a "thank you," he rose. "I see Drayton yonder," he said and moved away.

Condell shook his head in wonder. "Saw ye ever his like for ill manners?" he asked.

"Saw ye ever his fellow for audacity? Will, take not to heart aught that he hath said. Better an hour of Shakespeare than ten days of Jonson!"

"His bark is worse than his bite," said Will. "He means well. He is troubled, knowing that he breasts too strong a tide and must drown at last. I like his spirit. And his unpolished manners offend me not; for I know whence they come. I respect a bricklayer who has become a poet. And though he scoffs at my plays, friends, I think he scorns them less than he would have us believe."

21. *Hopes and Fears*

WILL could not but admit to himself that Jonson had a point about cross-wooing and clowns. "In all justice 'twas a fair shaft at my *Twelfth Night*," he said. "But what care I for the plot? If the play pleases, I am content."

As for what Jonson said of character, Will did not give it a second thought. He didn't want to teach; he wanted to delight, to enchant, to thrill. He had no interest in filling the stage with lifeless qualities masquerading as men. In comedy as in tragedy he wanted real people— with virtues and faults and human contradictions. Character absorbed him above all else.

At the moment he was creating someone far more interesting than either Antony or Brutus. And nothing Will had ever done had given him quite such satisfaction. He had taken the story of the new play from an old thriller, written by he knew not whom—a revenge play with a ghost and a murder and madness and the stage piled high with corpses at the end. Hamlet, Prince of Denmark, was the hero. Will was making of him a man who looked deep into himself and profoundly out on life. It gave him a chance to express many of the things he himself had been longing to say, and part of his satisfaction lay in that.

But only part. Will had a delightful sense of power as he worked on the play. Looking back at some of his old things, he was pleased to see how his poetry had improved. It was richer, grander, more controlled. He no longer let himself break out into flowery passages that only cluttered the play. Every line the hero spoke revealed new depths of his character. Every word was something the audience would carry away and think about. Will himself was thrilled by the mood he was managing to get into the play. And he thought excitedly: "The spectators will answer to it. I know my audience. They will lose themselves in the tragedy of this young Hamlet who must avenge his father's murder and cannot bring himself to do it. I see them already torn with pity and terror as I intend they shall be."

Will was sure he was writing a play that would draw crowds and be a money-maker. But he had no idea he was writing the greatest play in the world. There was no one to tell him so. No one who saw Richard Burbage play Hamlet guessed that for centuries to come every great actor's highest ambition would be to play that part. Of all the spectators at the Globe, perhaps only Ben Jonson quite realized how great *Hamlet* was. And he said nothing.

Young Hamlet must avenge his father's murder

On the 19th of March in the year 1603 Will Shakespeare went as usual to rehearsal—but there was no rehearsal. The theaters had been ordered closed. Old Queen Elizabeth, who had so loved plays, was deathly ill.

When on the 24th she passed away, a strange numbness settled over the city. The Queen had ruled for nearly half a century—it seemed impossible that England could get on without her. Will and his comrades, who had so often played before Elizabeth, felt the numbness even more than the rest. But mixed with it was apprehension. What would happen to them now that their great patroness was dead?

They felt as if a main support had given way under them. For they well knew that many a time only the Queen's love for plays had kept the theaters open. For years the Puritans had been fighting them. In their eyes plays were snares of the devil, and theaters temples of sin. The playhouses drew apprentices from work. They lured people from the churches. "Thick and threefold the folk run to those gorgeous playing places," the Puritans complained. "An hour's tolling of the bell bringeth but a scant hundred into church, while a thousand answer to the blowing of the trumpet that announceth the opening of a play."

And the Puritans were not the only ones who regarded the theaters with an unfavorable eye. Six years before, the Privy Council had well nigh put an end to them altogether. That was when the Lord Pembroke's Men had had the bad judgment to put on a play making fun of some notables. In its first fury the Council had ordered every theater pulled down. Luckily the Lord Chamberlain and the Lord Admiral were both members of the Council and, with the Queen backing them, had prevailed on the Council to relent. The theaters had been merely closed for a time. And two of the leading actors, along with Ben Jonson, who had written most of the play, had been marched off to prison.

How did James VI of Scotland—now to be James I of England—feel about theaters? The actors knew nothing about their new ruler except that he had been brought up in the Scottish church, which strongly disapproved of plays. Their art, their livelihood, their hopes hung in the balance—their future depended on the unknown tastes of a single man. Would James protect the theaters or not?

For six weeks the Lord Chamberlain's men waited anxiously to learn their fate. Then suddenly the tension broke—a summons to the court had come. The entire company were to be sworn in as the King's own royal servants! They would be styled Grooms of the Chamber and would play before the King whenever he pleased to command them. The Globe was safe. They would go on there as they had before—only henceforth they would be known as the King's Men.

22. *The Wonderful Years*

WILL SHAKESPEARE had just passed his thirty-ninth birthday when this happy news came. He was in the full command of his powers. And now there burst from him such a succession of wonderful plays that even his company, used as they were to great things from Will, marveled. In four brief years he gave them *Othello, King Lear, Macbeth, Antony and Cleopatra.* Their theater was always packed.

Henslowe had long ago run away from the competition of the Globe. He had abandoned the Rose and built the Fortune on the other side of the city, as far from Will as he could get. But even there he could not make a go of things. In despair he had called Ned Alleyn back from retirement, and for a while Ned had appeared again in some of his old Marlowe roles. But now Henslowe had nothing to offer. And meantime across the Thames the King's Men with their magician Will Shakespeare were drawing multitudes.

Ben Jonson, who never missed Will's plays, was bewildered. How was it possible for plays to succeed when every rule the Roman writers had laid down was broken? Will mixed comedy and tragedy in the same play. He would let a play cover months of time. He would have one scene in Egypt and the next one in Rome. He paid no attention to the unities at all. And yet it didn't seem to matter. Jonson had to admit it didn't seem to matter. The London audiences, who were bored with his correct plays, breathlessly watched the plays of Will Shakespeare, who didn't follow rules at all.

Will and his audience understood each other. And the same was true of Will and his players.

He never failed to ask for all that a man could give, and he never demanded more than a man could rise to. There was no friction between them. The players were gloriously proud of Will, and he was equally proud of them.

Especially was there a wonderful give and take between Will and Richard Burbage. Back in the days when he had first become a sharer, Will had thought, "What things Richard and I will do together!" And he had judged right. Richard rose to the greatness of each role Will created for him. He grasped every shade of meaning in his lines. Sometimes he even found meaning that Will himself was not conscious of. Richard needed no coaching. He knew by instinct what pitch or tone of his wonderful voice to use. He knew when to measure every word and when to hurry his pace. His silences were perfectly timed. His gestures, always exactly right, held the audience spellbound. His majestic presence filled the Globe.

"You inspire me, Richard," Will would say to him sometimes. "I dare the things I dare

Shakespeare's Globe Theater was always packed

only because I know you will carry them off with glory."

"Ah, Will," Richard would answer, "you force me to stand a-tiptoe to reach the stars. And I live only when I am reaching."

Chance had brought playwright and actor together in a golden moment of time. They

were a team such as the world had never known
and perhaps would never know again. Behind
them stood a disciplined and devoted company.
And among them all, the Globe was making
history.

23. *"Not One, but a Thousand Lives"*

IN THE fall of the year 1611, Will Shakespeare was riding toward Stratford. He was tired, tired. Though he was but forty-seven, his shoulders drooped under the weight of a quarter century in workaday London. The hair showing under his plumed hat was specked with gray. His face, distinguished by its high forehead, from which the once clustering curls

had fled, was heavily lined. But worn and weary
as he looked, there was sparkle in his eye and
a smile on his lips—Will's heart was set for
home.

"I should have gone years ago," he thought
as the familiar landscape seized intolerably on
his spirit. The fields were touched with frost,
the hedgerows brown and shriveled, the trees
bare. "Too many fair springs and summers
have I missed! I have not drunk deep of
meadows painted with delight. And here now
the winter cometh. Soon icicles will hang by
the wall."

How many times in the last four years he
had tried to make the break! But always the
cry had been, "We cannot spare you, Will! Stay
but one year more!" And he had yielded. Day
after day he had gone to the Globe and played
his part. Night after night he had labored to
give his company plays that would draw the
multitude. He was tired, tired. Even they who
urged him most to stay had realized at last that
he must go. He had remained only to see them
through *The Tempest,* then sold his shares

back to the company and, weeping unasham-
edly, wished his comrades well.

As his horse trotted along, Will could not
but recall that other journey he had made
twenty-five years before when for the first time
he rode away to London. Was that youth of
twenty-two, so filled with fire, so eager for life,
so mad about the theater, so unsure yet so determined, indeed himself? It seemed impossible that so many years lay between that Will
Shakespeare and this. A tender pity welled up
in him for the raw youth he had been. "Ah, lad,
you little knew what you were doing when you
sold your heart to make-believe," he thought.
"Where has your life gone? It has sped like a
dream, flashed by like lightning that is gone
ere one can say, 'It lightens.' "

And yet, looking back over the crowded
years, it seemed to him a century lay between
that young Will Shakespeare and himself.
Every day of the interval had been stretched to
the limit and its every hour filled with rich experience. Was there a thought he had not pon-
dered? Was there an emotion he had not felt?

At last Will Shakespeare was going back to Stratford

"I have lived not one, but a thousand lives," Will thought. "I have been every character in my every play. For, alas! I cannot, like God, breathe life into my creatures' nostrils with a puff. To make a man live, I must creep into his skin, look out of his eyes, behold the world, mankind, and himself as he seeth them, and explore each secret corner of his heart and mind. I have *been* Brutus, Hamlet, Othello, Lear, Macbeth, Antony, and all the rest. 'Gentle Will' they call me. But is there any violence, is there any passion I have not known? These hands stabbed Caesar. This heart is Hamlet's that did plot the death of Claudius. Macbeth and I together murdered Duncan. I have leaned with Othello over Desdemona's bed and stopped her innocent breath. With old King Lear I have disowned my best-beloved Cordelia. Antony and I together reveled late o' nights and thought the world well lost for Cleopatra. Love, hate, joy, grief, ambition, jealousy, remorse—I have known them all."

Two journeys and his life's work between. What had he to show for twenty-five years?

Three dozen plays. Two long poems. Some shorter poems. A hundred and fifty-four sonnets. Besides that, countless plays cut and adapted. Besides that, countless parts played. Last, but not least—a living earned and money put by. Will squared his shoulders at the thought of this homecoming, so different from his going away. He had won honor, love, obedience, troops of friends. He was returning a man of substance, a gentleman. He was going to live in New Place, the big, handsome house of his dreams, where already for some years Anne had been installed. It was a pity his father and mother were dead. But they had made their peace with the stage—for he had erased the stain of vagabondage from his name.

He was nearing the Avon now. Familiarly his eyes rested on the weeping willows that dipped their leafless branches in its waters. "Bare ruined choirs, where late the sweet birds sang," he thought, "I shall have time henceforth to watch you putting on your green attire. The hurly-burly of my life is done. I am for home, peace, night-rest, neighborhood."

Epilogue

IN THE month of April in the year 1621 John Heminges and Henry Condell sat with Ben Jonson in his house in Blackfriars. Their talk was of Will Shakespeare.

"We thought it right," Heminges said, "you having been his friend——"

"And being a poet and playmaker yourself," Condell put in.

"——to come to you rather than another. 'Tis five years this month that Will passed away."

"Speak not of it!" Ben Jonson said. "Ever it pains me to recall that Drayton and I were with him two days before he died. . . . But what would ye of me?"

Heminges' face assumed a yet greater earnestness as he leaned forward and said, "Harry here and I are set in our minds to do an office to the dead. We mean to care for his orphans, Ben."

"His orphans?" Ben echoed in astonishment.

"His *plays*," Condell explained with a smile. "The King's Men have all Will's playbooks, Ben. Divers of them have been published singly as you know—stolen, maimed, deformed. We mean to make a monument to Will—publish all his true plays, as he writ them, in a Folio."

"Not for ambition or self-profit," Heminges hastened to say.

"No, nor for fame. But only to keep the memory of so worthy a friend and fellow alive, as was our Will Shakespeare."

Ben Jonson was silent, thinking. "'Tis a noble thought," he said at last, "and worthy of Will's friends. But what desire ye of me?"

"A word of commendation, Ben, to go in front—a warm and personal estimate," John Heminges said. "Something from you would carry weight. 'Twill be a costly venture for us."

"I loved the man," Jonson said slowly. "And I honor his memory as much as any. But I was critical of his work. Yourselves have heard me oft. He had no art. . . . You have all his plays?"

"Six-and-thirty," Heminges said. "In very good condition all."

"Ay," said Condell, "what Will thought, he uttered with that easiness, that we have scarce received from him a blot in his papers."

"Bring them to me, then," said Jonson. "He hath not written by the rule, but what I can with honesty say in Shakespeare's praise, I will. . . ."

Afterwards when Ben looked back on that fortnight of reading, he felt it to be a time in his life apart. Something hard and rigid in him gave way. He swallowed the plays one after another almost without pausing, and each time he finished one he marveled more. "Rules are for lesser men," he said with a sigh. "What life, what life is here!"

When the last play had been read, Ben picked up his pen almost feverishly. How would he find the right words to sum up the impact the thirty-six plays had had on him? He was bewildered by the richness of the poetry, the wealth of lifelike characters, the depth of the thinking, the wit, the emotion, the imagination. He felt exhilarated, he felt enlarged. "O for a muse of fire," he exclaimed, "that I might do justice to this swan of Avon, this star of poets!"

Ben Jonson had never had his heart so much in anything as when he sat sweating out his tribute:

> Soul of the age,
> The applause! delight! the wonder of our
>   stage . . . .
> Thou art a monument without a tomb,
> And art alive still, while Thy Book doth live
> And we have wits to read and praise to give . . . .
> He was not of an age, but for all time.

When the poem was done and he had inscribed it

To the memory of my beloved, the Author,
  Mr. William Shakespeare
  And what he hath left us

Ben's only regret was that Will was not there to hear it.

"Blind, blind," he said as he laid down his quill. "A god walked amongst us, and we knew it not."

Index

179